THIS JOURNAL BELONGS TO SOMEONE AMAZING.
PLEASE RESPECT THEIR PRIVACY

If found, please return it to:

....

....

....

"We need to do a better job of putting ourselves
higher on our own 'to do' list."
– Michelle Obama

"YOUR JOURNAL
IS LIKE YOUR
BEST FRIEND,
YOU DON'T HAVE
TO PRETEND WITH IT,
YOU CAN BE HONEST
AND WRITE EXACTLY
HOW YOU FEEL"

BECOMING YOU SELF-HELP JOURNAL

Welcome!

The *Becoming You* journal is based on real-world experience and concepts designed to support you in organizing your thoughts and emotions.

It will help you track your goals and accomplishments, inspire you to Dreamcast your future, record how you have spent your life, and can help you heal from past traumas.

It doesn't matter what stage of life you are in, journaling is a powerful tool to support you in becoming the best you that YOU can be.

Journaling is a means of documenting your amazing life, just like the great journaling leaders of our time.

You are now part of a global community that has discovered the power of journaling.

Start your journey today to a happier and healthier you.

Enjoy the journey, enjoy becoming the best you.

Join our Discord Community of people who believe they are destined for more.

Free inspirational content, book downlods and more.

We are here to support you on your journey to the best YOU.

HOW TO USE YOUR JOURNAL

Where to start.

Step 1 - Your *Becoming You* journal starts with a graphic representation of your life in weeks.
Your life is precious and amazing. Take some time to work out which week of your life you are in at:
https://www.dreamcastproject.com/life.html

Step 2 - The *Becoming You* journal is divided into weeks, just like your life. Every week starts with a weekly topic to keep you on track to discovering and manifesting your best self.
Come back to these sections each week or anytime to see how you have grown.

Step 3 - The power of journaling comes from consistency.
We included a daily quote by leaders of color to inspire you to journal daily. Each day there is space to reflect and write down your emotions, what you are grateful for, your success affirmations, and space for your inspiring ideas for creating your amazing future, all while living your best life every day.

Becoming You Journal:

A powerful 12-week journal designed to help you achieve anything you put your mind to.

For more inspirational content, visit our blog.

www.dreamcastproject.com

"Fill your paper with the breathings of your heart."
- William Wordsworth.

THE STRUCTURE

Weekly: Each week starts with a new topic.

There are 12 topics to inspire you, motivate you, and support you in becoming your best self.

Your life is all-encompassing, and your journal should be too. This is why we created the Becoming You journal.

Your journal is designed to support your big and small goals and your personal growth and to help you reflect on your past accomplishments. Accomplishments that will fuel your future success.

Daily: 15 mins a day is all it takes to boldly manifest your hopes and dreams.

How I'm feeling today - a simple checklist of emotions as your starting point. There's extra space to add your own.

Why I'm feeling this way today - an essential part of working through how you feel. Supporting a healthy mind.

Reflecting on the good/gratitude - balance is essential for a healthy mind and it all starts with gratitude.
Reflecting on past accomplishments will help fuel your future.

How I spent my life force today - reflecting how you spent your precious time. An insightful and powerful exercise.

Ideation and future creation - great ideas are often lost when not written down. There is a reason why successful people keep a notepad on their bedside table.

Affirming great things in your life - Affirmations are powerful and can project you to your fullest potential

Quote for the day - to inspire you to your own greatness.

"Structure builds minds into great Monuments."
— Robert M. Hensel

Your "Becoming You" journal is more than just a journal, it has 12 powerful topics to support you in becoming the best version of yourself.

Weekly Topics:

You are now part of a global community that has discovered the power of journaling.

So go on, put pen to paper and let the magic happen.

Take some time to work out which week of your life you are in
https://www.dreamcastproject.com/life.html

*"It is not that we have a short time to live,
but that we waste a lot of it. Life is long enough,
and a sufficiently generous amount has
been given to us for the highest
achievements if it were all well invested.
Life is long if you know how to use it."
- Seneca*

MY LIFE IN WEEKS

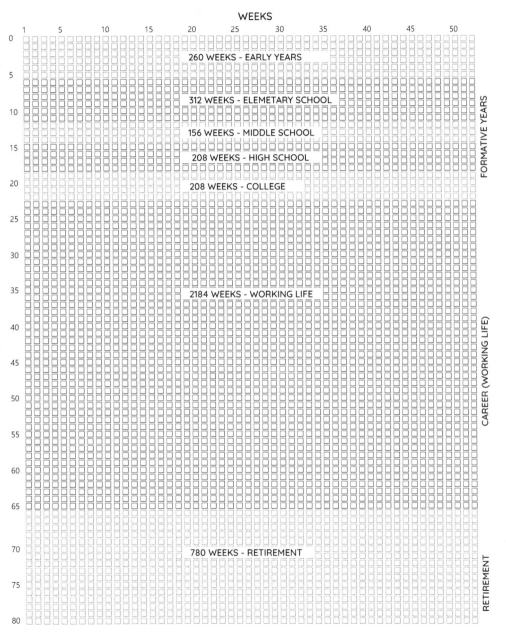

WEEKS

260 WEEKS - EARLY YEARS

312 WEEKS - ELEMETARY SCHOOL

156 WEEKS - MIDDLE SCHOOL

208 WEEKS - HIGH SCHOOL

208 WEEKS - COLLEGE

2184 WEEKS - WORKING LIFE

780 WEEKS - RETIREMENT

FORMATIVE YEARS

CAREER (WORKING LIFE)

RETIREMENT

YEARS

80 YEARS = WEEKS 4,160

WHO ARE YOU?

WEEK # _ _ _ _

Let's get to know you, the real you, not the you, you think you need to be.

This may seem silly, but give it a go. Your answers may surprise you.

It will also bring into focus all the awesome things that make you, you. Every part of you makes you worthy of what your amazing life has to offer.

This could be one of the hardest or easiest exercises in your journal.

Let's find out.

1. What three adjectives describe you best?

2. What makes you happy?

3. What is your biggest dream in life?

4. What do you lie about and why?

5. What are you the most proud of?

5. What would you change about yourself if you could?

_____

_____

_____

6. What are you most worried about?

_____

_____

_____

7. If you didn't have to sleep, what would you do with the extra time?

_____

_____

_____

8. What is one thing you would do if it would be impossible to fail?

_____

_____

_____

9. What is your definition of success?

_____

_____

_____

"I slept and dreamt that life was joy. I awoke and saw that life was service.
I acted and behold, service was joy." – Rabindranath Tagore

Keep going on your journey of knowing who your are...

"Never be limited by other people's limited imaginations."
– Dr. Mae Jemison

Date: _____   Week: #

How I'm feeling today.

☐ Positive   ☐ Confident   ☐ Stressed   ☐ Restless
☐ Happy   ☐ Excited   ☐ Frustrated   ☐ Trapped
☐ Hopeful   ☐ Determined   ☐ Sad   ☐ Bitter
☐ Grateful   ☐ Brave   ☐ Overwhelmed   ☐ Shocked
☐ Content   ☐ Inspired   ☐ Angry   ☐ Guilty
☐ Alive   ☐ Proud   ☐ Nervous   ☐ Unsure
☐   ☐   ☐   ☐

Why I am feeling this way today.

_____

_____

_____

_____

_____

_____

_____

_____

_____

Reflecting on the good. What can you be grateful for today?

_____

_____

_____

_____

Date: Week: #

How I spent my life force today.

_____

_____

_____

_____

_____

_____

_____

_____

_____

Affirming the great things in your life.

_____

_____

_____

_____

Ideation and future creation. Write down your inspiring ideas.

_____

_____

_____

_____

"Why do anything unless it is going to be great?"
– Peter Block

Date: Week: #

How I'm feeling today.

- [ ] Positive
- [ ] Happy
- [ ] Hopeful
- [ ] Grateful
- [ ] Content
- [ ] Alive
- [ ]

- [ ] Confident
- [ ] Excited
- [ ] Determined
- [ ] Brave
- [ ] Inspired
- [ ] Proud
- [ ]

- [ ] Stressed
- [ ] Frustrated
- [ ] Sad
- [ ] Overwhelmed
- [ ] Angry
- [ ] Nervous
- [ ]

- [ ] Restless
- [ ] Trapped
- [ ] Bitter
- [ ] Shocked
- [ ] Guilty
- [ ] Unsure
- [ ]

Why I am feeling this way today.

_____

_____

_____

_____

_____

_____

_____

_____

_____

_____

Reflecting on the good. What can you be grateful for today?

_____

_____

_____

_____

Date: Week: #

How I spent my life force today.

Affirming the great things in your life.

Ideation and future creation. Write down your inspiring ideas.

"You can't use up creativity. The more you use, the more you have."
– Maya Angelou

How I'm feeling today.

☐ Positive	☐ Confident	☐ Stressed	☐ Restless
☐ Happy	☐ Excited	☐ Frustrated	☐ Trapped
☐ Hopeful	☐ Determined	☐ Sad	☐ Bitter
☐ Grateful	☐ Brave	☐ Overwhelmed	☐ Shocked
☐ Content	☐ Inspired	☐ Angry	☐ Guilty
☐ Alive	☐ Proud	☐ Nervous	☐ Unsure
☐	☐	☐	☐

Why I am feeling this way today.

_____

_____

_____

_____

_____

_____

_____

_____

_____

Reflecting on the good. What can you be grateful for today?

_____

_____

_____

_____

Date: Week: #

How I spent my life force today.

_____

_____

_____

_____

_____

_____

_____

_____

_____

Affirming the great things in your life.

_____

_____

_____

Ideation and future creation. Write down your inspiring ideas.

_____

_____

_____

_____

"Life is not a spectator sport. If you're going to spend your whole life in the grandstand just watching what goes on, in my opinion, you're wasting your life." —Jackie Robinson

Date: _____   Week: #

How I'm feeling today.

☐ Positive   ☐ Confident   ☐ Stressed   ☐ Restless
☐ Happy   ☐ Excited   ☐ Frustrated   ☐ Trapped
☐ Hopeful   ☐ Determined   ☐ Sad   ☐ Bitter
☐ Grateful   ☐ Brave   ☐ Overwhelmed   ☐ Shocked
☐ Content   ☐ Inspired   ☐ Angry   ☐ Guilty
☐ Alive   ☐ Proud   ☐ Nervous   ☐ Unsure
☐   ☐   ☐   ☐

Why I am feeling this way today.

_____

_____

_____

_____

_____

_____

_____

_____

_____

Reflecting on the good. What can you be grateful for today?

_____

_____

_____

_____

Date: Week: #

How I spent my life force today.

Affirming the great things in your life.

Ideation and future creation. Write down your inspiring ideas.

"I am lucky that whatever fear I have inside me, my desire to win is always stronger."
—Serena Williams

Date: Week: #

How I'm feeling today.

- [ ] Positive
- [ ] Happy
- [ ] Hopeful
- [ ] Grateful
- [ ] Content
- [ ] Alive
- [ ]

- [ ] Confident
- [ ] Excited
- [ ] Determined
- [ ] Brave
- [ ] Inspired
- [ ] Proud
- [ ]

- [ ] Stressed
- [ ] Frustrated
- [ ] Sad
- [ ] Overwhelmed
- [ ] Angry
- [ ] Nervous
- [ ]

- [ ] Restless
- [ ] Trapped
- [ ] Bitter
- [ ] Shocked
- [ ] Guilty
- [ ] Unsure
- [ ]

Why I am feeling this way today.

Reflecting on the good. What can you be grateful for today?

Date: Week: #

How I spent my life force today.

_____

_____

_____

_____

_____

_____

_____

Affirming the great things in your life.

_____

_____

_____

Ideation and future creation. Write down your inspiring ideas.

_____

_____

_____

_____

"If they don't give you a seat at the table, bring a folding chair."
—Shirley Chisholm

Date: _____   Week: #

How I'm feeling today.

☐ Positive	☐ Confident	☐ Stressed	☐ Restless
☐ Happy	☐ Excited	☐ Frustrated	☐ Trapped
☐ Hopeful	☐ Determined	☐ Sad	☐ Bitter
☐ Grateful	☐ Brave	☐ Overwhelmed	☐ Shocked
☐ Content	☐ Inspired	☐ Angry	☐ Guilty
☐ Alive	☐ Proud	☐ Nervous	☐ Unsure
☐	☐	☐	☐

Why I am feeling this way today.

_____

_____

_____

_____

_____

_____

_____

_____

_____

Reflecting on the good. What can you be grateful for today?

_____

_____

_____

_____

Date: Week: #

How I spent my life force today.

Affirming the great things in your life.

Ideation and future creation. Write down your inspiring ideas.

How I'm feeling today.

☐ Positive	☐ Confident	☐ Stressed	☐ Restless
☐ Happy	☐ Excited	☐ Frustrated	☐ Trapped
☐ Hopeful	☐ Determined	☐ Sad	☐ Bitter
☐ Grateful	☐ Brave	☐ Overwhelmed	☐ Shocked
☐ Content	☐ Inspired	☐ Angry	☐ Guilty
☐ Alive	☐ Proud	☐ Nervous	☐ Unsure
☐	☐	☐	☐

Why I am feeling this way today.

Reflecting on the good. What can you be grateful for today?

How I spent my life force today.

Affirming the great things in your life.

Ideation and future creation. Write down your inspiring ideas.

"The visionary starts with a clean sheet of paper, and re-imagines the world.."
– Malcolm Gladwell

YOUR WHY

WEEK # _ _ _ _

Journaling is one of the best tools to help discover your why.

It's an amazing way to tap into your own inner wisdom. You'll find that the answers and solutions you discover through journaling are both insightful and powerful - and they work.

When you know your why, it becomes easier to focus on where you are going, what matters most in your life, and what decisions are aligned with your goals.

This week, uncover your why by asking yourself what you want. When you have the answer, go deeper and ask: "Why your [answer] is important to you?"

Repeat the process up to seven times until you reach the answer that most profoundly resonates with you.

It will give you clarity on why you do what you do. Clarity leads to inspired action, inspired action leads to you operating from your deepest conviction.
Think about what it is you want, and ask yourself the following.

YOUR WHY

What do I want?

Answer :

Question #1: What about [Thing I want:] is important to me?

Answer 1:

Question #2: Why is [answer 1] important to me?

Answer 2:

Question #3: Why is [answer 2] important to me?

Answer 3:

Question #4: Why is [answer 3] important to me?

Answer 4:

Question #5: Why is [answer 4] important to me?

Answer 5:

Question #6: Why is [answer 5] important to me?

Answer 6:

Question #7: Why is [answer 6] important to me?

Answer: 7

"No solution can ever be found by running in three different directions."
– Deepak Chopra

"Do not dwell in the past, do not dream of the future, concentrate the mind on the present moment."
– Buddha

How I'm feeling today.

- ☐ Positive
- ☐ Happy
- ☐ Hopeful
- ☐ Grateful
- ☐ Content
- ☐ Alive
- ☐

- ☐ Confident
- ☐ Excited
- ☐ Determined
- ☐ Brave
- ☐ Inspired
- ☐ Proud
- ☐

- ☐ Stressed
- ☐ Frustrated
- ☐ Sad
- ☐ Overwhelmed
- ☐ Angry
- ☐ Nervous
- ☐

- ☐ Restless
- ☐ Trapped
- ☐ Bitter
- ☐ Shocked
- ☐ Guilty
- ☐ Unsure
- ☐

Why I am feeling this way today.

_____

_____

_____

_____

_____

_____

_____

_____

_____

_____

Reflecting on the good. What can you be grateful for today?

_____

_____

_____

_____

Date: Week: #

How I spent my life force today.

Affirming the great things in your life.

Ideation and future creation. Write down your inspiring ideas.

"If you wake up deciding what you want to give versus what you're going to get, you become a more successful person." –Russell Simmons

Date: Week: #

How I'm feeling today.

- ☐ Positive
- ☐ Happy
- ☐ Hopeful
- ☐ Grateful
- ☐ Content
- ☐ Alive
- ☐

- ☐ Confident
- ☐ Excited
- ☐ Determined
- ☐ Brave
- ☐ Inspired
- ☐ Proud
- ☐

- ☐ Stressed
- ☐ Frustrated
- ☐ Sad
- ☐ Overwhelmed
- ☐ Angry
- ☐ Nervous
- ☐

- ☐ Restless
- ☐ Trapped
- ☐ Bitter
- ☐ Shocked
- ☐ Guilty
- ☐ Unsure
- ☐

Why I am feeling this way today.

Reflecting on the good. What can you be grateful for today?

Date: Week: #

How I spent my life force today.

_____

_____

_____

_____

_____

_____

_____

_____

Affirming the great things in your life.

_____

_____

_____

_____

Ideation and future creation. Write down your inspiring ideas.

_____

_____

_____

_____

"A life is not important except in the impact it has on other lives."
-Jackie Robinson

Date: _____   Week: #

How I'm feeling today.

- [ ] Positive
- [ ] Happy
- [ ] Hopeful
- [ ] Grateful
- [ ] Content
- [ ] Alive
- [ ]

- [ ] Confident
- [ ] Excited
- [ ] Determined
- [ ] Brave
- [ ] Inspired
- [ ] Proud
- [ ]

- [ ] Stressed
- [ ] Frustrated
- [ ] Sad
- [ ] Overwhelmed
- [ ] Angry
- [ ] Nervous
- [ ]

- [ ] Restless
- [ ] Trapped
- [ ] Bitter
- [ ] Shocked
- [ ] Guilty
- [ ] Unsure
- [ ]

Why I am feeling this way today.

_____

_____

_____

_____

_____

_____

_____

_____

_____

_____

Reflecting on the good. What can you be grateful for today?

_____

_____

_____

_____

Date:

How I spent my life force today.

_____

_____

_____

_____

_____

_____

_____

_____

Affirming the great things in your life.

_____

_____

_____

Ideation and future creation. Write down your inspiring ideas.

_____

_____

_____

_____

_____

"Darkness cannot drive out darkness; only light can do that. Hate cannot drive out hate; only love can do that." –Martin Luther King Jr.

How I'm feeling today.

- ☐ Positive
- ☐ Happy
- ☐ Hopeful
- ☐ Grateful
- ☐ Content
- ☐ Alive
- ☐

- ☐ Confident
- ☐ Excited
- ☐ Determined
- ☐ Brave
- ☐ Inspired
- ☐ Proud
- ☐

- ☐ Stressed
- ☐ Frustrated
- ☐ Sad
- ☐ Overwhelmed
- ☐ Angry
- ☐ Nervous
- ☐

- ☐ Restless
- ☐ Trapped
- ☐ Bitter
- ☐ Shocked
- ☐ Guilty
- ☐ Unsure
- ☐

Why I am feeling this way today.

_____

_____

_____

_____

_____

_____

_____

_____

_____

_____

Reflecting on the good. What can you be grateful for today?

_____

_____

_____

_____

Date: Week: #

How I spent my life force today.

Affirming the great things in your life.

Ideation and future creation. Write down your inspiring ideas.

Date: _____   Week: #

How I'm feeling today.

☐ Positive	☐ Confident	☐ Stressed	☐ Restless
☐ Happy	☐ Excited	☐ Frustrated	☐ Trapped
☐ Hopeful	☐ Determined	☐ Sad	☐ Bitter
☐ Grateful	☐ Brave	☐ Overwhelmed	☐ Shocked
☐ Content	☐ Inspired	☐ Angry	☐ Guilty
☐ Alive	☐ Proud	☐ Nervous	☐ Unsure
☐	☐	☐	☐

Why I am feeling this way today.

_____

_____

_____

_____

_____

_____

_____

_____

Reflecting on the good. What can you be grateful for today?

_____

_____

_____

_____

Date: Week: #

How I spent my life force today.

Affirming the great things in your life.

Ideation and future creation. Write down your inspiring ideas.

"We all require and want respect, man or woman, black or white. It's our basic human right."
—Aretha Franklin

Date: _____   Week: #

How I'm feeling today.

☐ Positive   ☐ Confident   ☐ Stressed   ☐ Restless
☐ Happy   ☐ Excited   ☐ Frustrated   ☐ Trapped
☐ Hopeful   ☐ Determined   ☐ Sad   ☐ Bitter
☐ Grateful   ☐ Brave   ☐ Overwhelmed   ☐ Shocked
☐ Content   ☐ Inspired   ☐ Angry   ☐ Guilty
☐ Alive   ☐ Proud   ☐ Nervous   ☐ Unsure
☐   ☐   ☐   ☐

Why I am feeling this way today.

_____

_____

_____

_____

_____

_____

_____

_____

_____

Reflecting on the good. What can you be grateful for today?

_____

_____

_____

_____

Date: Week: #

How I spent my life force today.

Affirming the great things in your life.

Ideation and future creation. Write down your inspiring ideas.

"The most common way people give up their power is by thinking they don't have any."
- Alice Walker

Date: _____   Week: #

How I'm feeling today.

☐ Positive   ☐ Confident   ☐ Stressed   ☐ Restless
☐ Happy   ☐ Excited   ☐ Frustrated   ☐ Trapped
☐ Hopeful   ☐ Determined   ☐ Sad   ☐ Bitter
☐ Grateful   ☐ Brave   ☐ Overwhelmed   ☐ Shocked
☐ Content   ☐ Inspired   ☐ Angry   ☐ Guilty
☐ Alive   ☐ Proud   ☐ Nervous   ☐ Unsure
☐   ☐   ☐   ☐

Why I am feeling this way today.

_____

_____

_____

_____

_____

_____

_____

_____

Reflecting on the good. What can you be grateful for today?

_____

_____

_____

_____

Date: Week: #

How I spent my life force today.

Affirming the great things in your life.

Ideation and future creation. Write down your inspiring ideas.

"Do the best you can until you know better. Then when you know better, do better."
—Maya Angelou

YOUR GOALS

WEEK # _ _ _ _

What goals are you working towards?
Big or small, write them all down.

Your journal is a way for you to start bringing your
dreams to life. Your goals and dreams started as a
thought. Now give them life in the form of writing and
bring them closer to reality.

There are many benefits and advantages to having a set
of goals to work towards.

Setting goals helps trigger new behaviors, helps guide
your focus, and helps you sustain momentum in life.

Goals also help align your focus and promote a sense of
self-mastery and accomplishment.

Use this section to add your goals and come back to
them anytime to track your progress.

YOUR GOALS

Your goals can have a lasting impact on your life and the lives of others.
They can be large goals, or they can be smaller more personal goals.
Write down the goals that come to mind. Start with short term goals [< 1 yr],
then move on to your long term goals [> 1 yr]. Think big, be unrealistic, it's ok!

"The first step is you have to say that you can."
– Will Smith

"Defining myself, as opposed to being defined by others,
is one of the most difficult challenges I face." –Carol Moseley-Braun

How I'm feeling today.

- ☐ Positive
- ☐ Happy
- ☐ Hopeful
- ☐ Grateful
- ☐ Content
- ☐ Alive
- ☐

- ☐ Confident
- ☐ Excited
- ☐ Determined
- ☐ Brave
- ☐ Inspired
- ☐ Proud
- ☐

- ☐ Stressed
- ☐ Frustrated
- ☐ Sad
- ☐ Overwhelmed
- ☐ Angry
- ☐ Nervous
- ☐

- ☐ Restless
- ☐ Trapped
- ☐ Bitter
- ☐ Shocked
- ☐ Guilty
- ☐ Unsure
- ☐

Why I am feeling this way today.

Reflecting on the good. What can you be grateful for today?

Date: Week: #

How I spent my life force today.

Affirming the great things in your life.

Ideation and future creation. Write down your inspiring ideas.

"Freeing yourself was one thing; claiming ownership of that freed self was another."
- Toni Morrison

Date: _____   Week: #

How I'm feeling today.

☐ Positive   ☐ Confident   ☐ Stressed   ☐ Restless
☐ Happy   ☐ Excited   ☐ Frustrated   ☐ Trapped
☐ Hopeful   ☐ Determined   ☐ Sad   ☐ Bitter
☐ Grateful   ☐ Brave   ☐ Overwhelmed   ☐ Shocked
☐ Content   ☐ Inspired   ☐ Angry   ☐ Guilty
☐ Alive   ☐ Proud   ☐ Nervous   ☐ Unsure
☐   ☐   ☐   ☐

Why I am feeling this way today.

_____

_____

_____

_____

_____

_____

_____

_____

_____

_____

Reflecting on the good. What can you be grateful for today?

_____

_____

_____

_____

Date: Week: #

How I spent my life force today.

_____

_____

_____

_____

_____

_____

_____

_____

_____

Affirming the great things in your life.

_____

_____

_____

Ideation and future creation. Write down your inspiring ideas.

_____

_____

_____

_____

_____

But dreams do not come true just because you dream them. It's hard work that
makes things happen. It's hard work that creates change." —Shonda Rhimes

Date: Week: #

How I'm feeling today.

- [ ] Positive
- [ ] Happy
- [ ] Hopeful
- [ ] Grateful
- [ ] Content
- [ ] Alive
- [ ]

- [ ] Confident
- [ ] Excited
- [ ] Determined
- [ ] Brave
- [ ] Inspired
- [ ] Proud
- [ ]

- [ ] Stressed
- [ ] Frustrated
- [ ] Sad
- [ ] Overwhelmed
- [ ] Angry
- [ ] Nervous
- [ ]

- [ ] Restless
- [ ] Trapped
- [ ] Bitter
- [ ] Shocked
- [ ] Guilty
- [ ] Unsure
- [ ]

Why I am feeling this way today.

_____

_____

_____

_____

_____

_____

_____

_____

Reflecting on the good. What can you be grateful for today?

_____

_____

_____

_____

Date: Week: #

How I spent my life force today.

Affirming the great things in your life.

Ideation and future creation. Write down your inspiring ideas.

How I'm feeling today.

☐ Positive   ☐ Confident   ☐ Stressed   ☐ Restless
☐ Happy   ☐ Excited   ☐ Frustrated   ☐ Trapped
☐ Hopeful   ☐ Determined   ☐ Sad   ☐ Bitter
☐ Grateful   ☐ Brave   ☐ Overwhelmed   ☐ Shocked
☐ Content   ☐ Inspired   ☐ Angry   ☐ Guilty
☐ Alive   ☐ Proud   ☐ Nervous   ☐ Unsure
☐   ☐   ☐   ☐

Why I am feeling this way today.

_____

_____

_____

_____

_____

_____

_____

_____

Reflecting on the good. What can you be grateful for today?

_____

_____

_____

_____

Date: Week: #

How I spent my life force today.

_____

_____

_____

_____

_____

_____

_____

_____

_____

Affirming the great things in your life.

_____

_____

_____

Ideation and future creation. Write down your inspiring ideas.

_____

_____

_____

_____

"Life has two rules: number 1, never quit! Number 2, always remember rule number one."
—Duke Ellington

Date: _____   Week: #

How I'm feeling today.

☐ Positive   ☐ Confident   ☐ Stressed   ☐ Restless
☐ Happy   ☐ Excited   ☐ Frustrated   ☐ Trapped
☐ Hopeful   ☐ Determined   ☐ Sad   ☐ Bitter
☐ Grateful   ☐ Brave   ☐ Overwhelmed   ☐ Shocked
☐ Content   ☐ Inspired   ☐ Angry   ☐ Guilty
☐ Alive   ☐ Proud   ☐ Nervous   ☐ Unsure
☐   ☐   ☐   ☐

Why I am feeling this way today.

_____

_____

_____

_____

_____

_____

_____

_____

_____

_____

Reflecting on the good. What can you be grateful for today?

_____

_____

_____

_____

Date: Week: #

How I spent my life force today.

_____

_____

_____

_____

_____

_____

_____

_____

_____

_____

Affirming the great things in your life.

_____

_____

_____

_____

Ideation and future creation. Write down your inspiring ideas.

_____

_____

_____

_____

_____

"Review your goals twice every day in order to be focused on achieving them."
– Les Brown

Date: Week: #

How I'm feeling today.

☐ Positive	☐ Confident	☐ Stressed	☐ Restless
☐ Happy	☐ Excited	☐ Frustrated	☐ Trapped
☐ Hopeful	☐ Determined	☐ Sad	☐ Bitter
☐ Grateful	☐ Brave	☐ Overwhelmed	☐ Shocked
☐ Content	☐ Inspired	☐ Angry	☐ Guilty
☐ Alive	☐ Proud	☐ Nervous	☐ Unsure
☐	☐	☐	☐

Why I am feeling this way today.

Reflecting on the good. What can you be grateful for today?

Date: Week: #

How I spent my life force today.

Affirming the great things in your life.

Ideation and future creation. Write down your inspiring ideas.

"All great achievements require time."
– Maya Angelou

How I'm feeling today.

- [ ] Positive
- [ ] Happy
- [ ] Hopeful
- [ ] Grateful
- [ ] Content
- [ ] Alive
- [ ]

- [ ] Confident
- [ ] Excited
- [ ] Determined
- [ ] Brave
- [ ] Inspired
- [ ] Proud
- [ ]

- [ ] Stressed
- [ ] Frustrated
- [ ] Sad
- [ ] Overwhelmed
- [ ] Angry
- [ ] Nervous
- [ ]

- [ ] Restless
- [ ] Trapped
- [ ] Bitter
- [ ] Shocked
- [ ] Guilty
- [ ] Unsure
- [ ]

Why I am feeling this way today.

_____

_____

_____

_____

_____

_____

_____

_____

_____

Reflecting on the good. What can you be grateful for today?

_____

_____

_____

_____

Date: Week: #

How I spent my life force today.

_____

_____

_____

_____

_____

_____

_____

_____

_____

Affirming the great things in your life.

_____

_____

_____

_____

Ideation and future creation. Write down your inspiring ideas.

_____

_____

_____

_____

"Writing in a journal reminds you of your goals and of your learning in life. It offers a place where you can hold a deliberate, thoughtful conversation with yourself." – Robin S. Sharma

MAKING ADJUSTMENTS

WEEK # _ _ _ _

Sometimes we just need a bit of reflection and Dream Casting to help us make small adjustments to create our best future life.

Let's do that now using the graphic on the next page.

1. Begin by reflecting on your current life, and write down where you are today. Your current life trajectory.

2. Then envision what your ideal life could look like as you see it from the present. Your future life trajectory.

3. Finally, the space between these two lines / lives reflects real opportunity on how you could reduce the gap and bring your present closer to your future life trajectory.

What possible adjustments could you make to bring your current life trajectory closer to your chosen future life trajectory? e.g., you may sharpen your skills in a specific area to change your career trajectory.

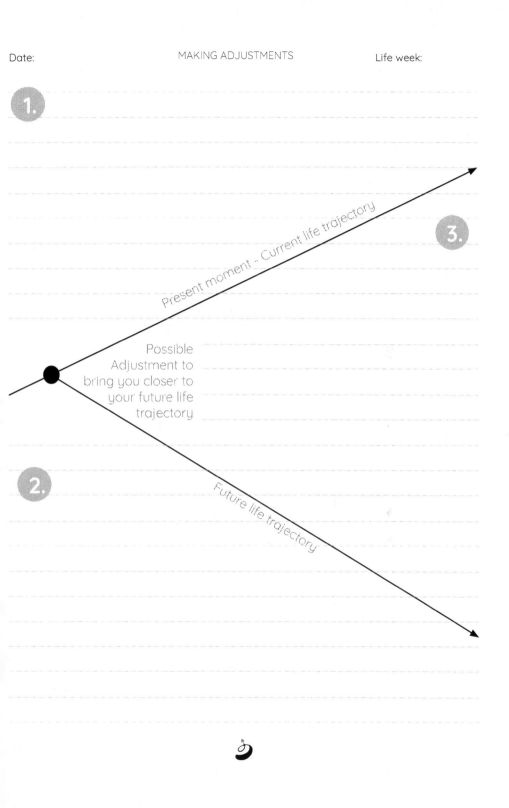

"There is no passion to be found playing small - in settling for a life that is less
than the one you are capable of living." – Nelson Mandela

"Passion is energy. Feel the power that comes from focusing on what excites you."
– Oprah Winfrey

How I'm feeling today.

- ☐ Positive
- ☐ Happy
- ☐ Hopeful
- ☐ Grateful
- ☐ Content
- ☐ Alive
- ☐

- ☐ Confident
- ☐ Excited
- ☐ Determined
- ☐ Brave
- ☐ Inspired
- ☐ Proud
- ☐

- ☐ Stressed
- ☐ Frustrated
- ☐ Sad
- ☐ Overwhelmed
- ☐ Angry
- ☐ Nervous
- ☐

- ☐ Restless
- ☐ Trapped
- ☐ Bitter
- ☐ Shocked
- ☐ Guilty
- ☐ Unsure
- ☐

Why I am feeling this way today.

Reflecting on the good. What can you be grateful for today?

Date: Week: #

How I spent my life force today.

Affirming the great things in your life.

Ideation and future creation. Write down your inspiring ideas.

"Change will not come if we wait for some other person or some other time.
We are the ones we've been waiting for. We are the change that we seek." –Barack Obama

How I'm feeling today.

☐ Positive   ☐ Confident   ☐ Stressed   ☐ Restless
☐ Happy   ☐ Excited   ☐ Frustrated   ☐ Trapped
☐ Hopeful   ☐ Determined   ☐ Sad   ☐ Bitter
☐ Grateful   ☐ Brave   ☐ Overwhelmed   ☐ Shocked
☐ Content   ☐ Inspired   ☐ Angry   ☐ Guilty
☐ Alive   ☐ Proud   ☐ Nervous   ☐ Unsure
☐   ☐   ☐   ☐

Why I am feeling this way today.

_____

_____

_____

_____

_____

_____

_____

_____

_____

Reflecting on the good. What can you be grateful for today?

_____

_____

_____

_____

Date: Week: #

How I spent my life force today.

_____

_____

_____

_____

_____

_____

_____

_____

Affirming the great things in your life.

_____

_____

_____

Ideation and future creation. Write down your inspiring ideas.

_____

_____

_____

_____

"A man without knowledge of himself and his heritage is like a tree without roots."
—Dick Gregory

How I'm feeling today.

- [ ] Positive
- [ ] Happy
- [ ] Hopeful
- [ ] Grateful
- [ ] Content
- [ ] Alive
- [ ]

- [ ] Confident
- [ ] Excited
- [ ] Determined
- [ ] Brave
- [ ] Inspired
- [ ] Proud
- [ ]

- [ ] Stressed
- [ ] Frustrated
- [ ] Sad
- [ ] Overwhelmed
- [ ] Angry
- [ ] Nervous
- [ ]

- [ ] Restless
- [ ] Trapped
- [ ] Bitter
- [ ] Shocked
- [ ] Guilty
- [ ] Unsure
- [ ]

Why I am feeling this way today.

_____

_____

_____

_____

_____

_____

_____

_____

_____

Reflecting on the good. What can you be grateful for today?

_____

_____

_____

_____

Date: Week: #

How I spent my life force today.

_____

_____

_____

_____

_____

_____

_____

_____

Affirming the great things in your life.

_____

_____

_____

Ideation and future creation. Write down your inspiring ideas.

_____

_____

_____

"We have a wonderful history behind us...and it is going to inspire us to greater achievements."
—Carter G. Woodson

Date: Week: #

How I'm feeling today.

☐ Positive	☐ Confident	☐ Stressed	☐ Restless
☐ Happy	☐ Excited	☐ Frustrated	☐ Trapped
☐ Hopeful	☐ Determined	☐ Sad	☐ Bitter
☐ Grateful	☐ Brave	☐ Overwhelmed	☐ Shocked
☐ Content	☐ Inspired	☐ Angry	☐ Guilty
☐ Alive	☐ Proud	☐ Nervous	☐ Unsure
☐	☐	☐	☐

Why I am feeling this way today.

Reflecting on the good. What can you be grateful for today?

Date: Week: #

How I spent my life force today.

_____

_____

_____

_____

_____

_____

_____

_____

_____

_____

Affirming the great things in your life.

_____

_____

_____

_____

Ideation and future creation. Write down your inspiring ideas.

_____

_____

_____

_____

_____

"You are your best thing."
—Toni Morrison

How I'm feeling today.

- ☐ Positive
- ☐ Happy
- ☐ Hopeful
- ☐ Grateful
- ☐ Content
- ☐ Alive
- ☐

- ☐ Confident
- ☐ Excited
- ☐ Determined
- ☐ Brave
- ☐ Inspired
- ☐ Proud
- ☐

- ☐ Stressed
- ☐ Frustrated
- ☐ Sad
- ☐ Overwhelmed
- ☐ Angry
- ☐ Nervous
- ☐

- ☐ Restless
- ☐ Trapped
- ☐ Bitter
- ☐ Shocked
- ☐ Guilty
- ☐ Unsure
- ☐

Why I am feeling this way today.

Reflecting on the good. What can you be grateful for today?

Date: _____   Week: #

How I spent my life force today.

_____

_____

_____

_____

_____

_____

_____

_____

Affirming the great things in your life.

_____

_____

_____

_____

Ideation and future creation. Write down your inspiring ideas.

_____

_____

_____

_____

_____

"A good head and a good heart are always a formidable combination."
—Nelson Mandela

How I'm feeling today.

☐ Positive   ☐ Confident   ☐ Stressed   ☐ Restless
☐ Happy   ☐ Excited   ☐ Frustrated   ☐ Trapped
☐ Hopeful   ☐ Determined   ☐ Sad   ☐ Bitter
☐ Grateful   ☐ Brave   ☐ Overwhelmed   ☐ Shocked
☐ Content   ☐ Inspired   ☐ Angry   ☐ Guilty
☐ Alive   ☐ Proud   ☐ Nervous   ☐ Unsure
☐   ☐   ☐   ☐

Why I am feeling this way today.

Reflecting on the good. What can you be grateful for today?

Date: Week: #

How I spent my life force today.

Affirming the great things in your life.

Ideation and future creation. Write down your inspiring ideas.

☽

"Writing in a journal reminds you of your goals and of your learning in life. It offers a place
where you can hold a deliberate, thoughtful conversation with yourself." - Robin S. Sharma

Date: Week: #

How I'm feeling today.

☐ Positive	☐ Confident	☐ Stressed	☐ Restless
☐ Happy	☐ Excited	☐ Frustrated	☐ Trapped
☐ Hopeful	☐ Determined	☐ Sad	☐ Bitter
☐ Grateful	☐ Brave	☐ Overwhelmed	☐ Shocked
☐ Content	☐ Inspired	☐ Angry	☐ Guilty
☐ Alive	☐ Proud	☐ Nervous	☐ Unsure
☐	☐	☐	☐

Why I am feeling this way today.

Reflecting on the good. What can you be grateful for today?

Date: Week: #

How I spent my life force today.

_____

_____

_____

_____

_____

_____

_____

_____

Affirming the great things in your life.

_____

_____

_____

_____

Ideation and future creation. Write down your inspiring ideas.

_____

_____

_____

_____

_____

"What keeps me going is goals."
- Muhammad Ali

PIECES OF THE WHOLE (PIE OF LIFE)

WEEK # _ _ _ _

Life is, by its very nature, multifaceted.

Reflecting on every facet of your life, knowing and accepting where you are right now is the first step to building the life you deserve.

The Pie of Life is a good indicator of:
1. where our time and energy are spent,
2. where we are most fulfilled.

It helps to make informed decisions that will bring more balance into our lives.

Set aside some quiet time – 20-30 minutes – to visualize the various facets that make up the pieces of the whole you.

Do this by shading in the areas you are most happy with on a scale of 1 -10. This will also highlight the areas in your life that may need some work.

Use the additional pages in this section for more self-reflection.

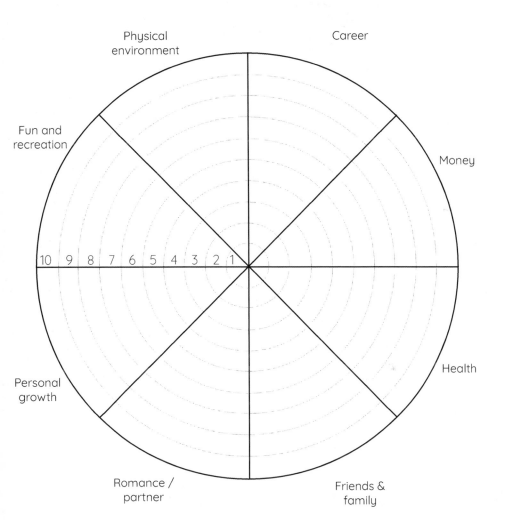

"You have power over your mind - not outside events.
Realize this, and you will find strength." - Marcus Aurelius

Date: PIE OF LIFE Week #:

Date: _____   Week: #

How I'm feeling today.

☐ Positive   ☐ Confident   ☐ Stressed   ☐ Restless
☐ Happy   ☐ Excited   ☐ Frustrated   ☐ Trapped
☐ Hopeful   ☐ Determined   ☐ Sad   ☐ Bitter
☐ Grateful   ☐ Brave   ☐ Overwhelmed   ☐ Shocked
☐ Content   ☐ Inspired   ☐ Angry   ☐ Guilty
☐ Alive   ☐ Proud   ☐ Nervous   ☐ Unsure
☐   ☐   ☐   ☐

Why I am feeling this way today.

_____

_____

_____

_____

_____

_____

_____

_____

_____

_____

Reflecting on the good. What can you be grateful for today?

_____

_____

_____

_____

Date: Week: #

How I spent my life force today.

_____

_____

_____

_____

_____

_____

_____

_____

Affirming the great things in your life.

_____

_____

_____

Ideation and future creation. Write down your inspiring ideas.

_____

_____

_____

_____

"It takes half your life before you discover life is a do-it-yourself project."
- Napoleon Hill

Date: Week: #

How I'm feeling today.

☐ Positive	☐ Confident	☐ Stressed	☐ Restless
☐ Happy	☐ Excited	☐ Frustrated	☐ Trapped
☐ Hopeful	☐ Determined	☐ Sad	☐ Bitter
☐ Grateful	☐ Brave	☐ Overwhelmed	☐ Shocked
☐ Content	☐ Inspired	☐ Angry	☐ Guilty
☐ Alive	☐ Proud	☐ Nervous	☐ Unsure
☐	☐	☐	☐

Why I am feeling this way today.

_____

_____

_____

_____

_____

_____

_____

_____

_____

Reflecting on the good. What can you be grateful for today?

_____

_____

_____

_____

Date: Week: #

How I spent my life force today.

Affirming the great things in your life.

Ideation and future creation. Write down your inspiring ideas.

"Your only limit is you."
– Unknown

How I'm feeling today.

☐ Positive   ☐ Confident   ☐ Stressed   ☐ Restless
☐ Happy   ☐ Excited   ☐ Frustrated   ☐ Trapped
☐ Hopeful   ☐ Determined   ☐ Sad   ☐ Bitter
☐ Grateful   ☐ Brave   ☐ Overwhelmed   ☐ Shocked
☐ Content   ☐ Inspired   ☐ Angry   ☐ Guilty
☐ Alive   ☐ Proud   ☐ Nervous   ☐ Unsure
☐   ☐   ☐   ☐

Why I am feeling this way today.

Reflecting on the good. What can you be grateful for today?

Date: Week: #

How I spent my life force today.

Affirming the great things in your life.

Ideation and future creation. Write down your inspiring ideas.

☽

"Always go with your passions. Never ask yourself if it's realistic or not."
– Deepak Chopra

How I'm feeling today.

- [ ] Positive
- [ ] Happy
- [ ] Hopeful
- [ ] Grateful
- [ ] Content
- [ ] Alive
- [ ]

- [ ] Confident
- [ ] Excited
- [ ] Determined
- [ ] Brave
- [ ] Inspired
- [ ] Proud
- [ ]

- [ ] Stressed
- [ ] Frustrated
- [ ] Sad
- [ ] Overwhelmed
- [ ] Angry
- [ ] Nervous
- [ ]

- [ ] Restless
- [ ] Trapped
- [ ] Bitter
- [ ] Shocked
- [ ] Guilty
- [ ] Unsure
- [ ]

Why I am feeling this way today.

_____

_____

_____

_____

_____

_____

_____

_____

_____

_____

Reflecting on the good. What can you be grateful for today?

_____

_____

_____

_____

Date: Week: #

How I spent my life force today.

Affirming the great things in your life.

Ideation and future creation. Write down your inspiring ideas.

"Let us always meet each other with smile, for the smile is the beginning of love."
– Mother Teresa

Date: _____   Week: #

How I'm feeling today.

☐ Positive   ☐ Confident   ☐ Stressed   ☐ Restless
☐ Happy   ☐ Excited   ☐ Frustrated   ☐ Trapped
☐ Hopeful   ☐ Determined   ☐ Sad   ☐ Bitter
☐ Grateful   ☐ Brave   ☐ Overwhelmed   ☐ Shocked
☐ Content   ☐ Inspired   ☐ Angry   ☐ Guilty
☐ Alive   ☐ Proud   ☐ Nervous   ☐ Unsure
☐   ☐   ☐   ☐

Why I am feeling this way today.

_____

_____

_____

_____

_____

_____

_____

_____

_____

Reflecting on the good. What can you be grateful for today?

_____

_____

_____

_____

Date: Week: #

How I spent my life force today.

_____

_____

_____

_____

_____

_____

_____

Affirming the great things in your life.

_____

_____

_____

Ideation and future creation. Write down your inspiring ideas.

_____

_____

_____

_____

"Life's like a play: it's not the length, but the excellence of the acting that matters."
- Lucius Annaeus Seneca

How I'm feeling today.

☐ Positive	☐ Confident	☐ Stressed	☐ Restless
☐ Happy	☐ Excited	☐ Frustrated	☐ Trapped
☐ Hopeful	☐ Determined	☐ Sad	☐ Bitter
☐ Grateful	☐ Brave	☐ Overwhelmed	☐ Shocked
☐ Content	☐ Inspired	☐ Angry	☐ Guilty
☐ Alive	☐ Proud	☐ Nervous	☐ Unsure
☐	☐	☐	☐

Why I am feeling this way today.

Reflecting on the good. What can you be grateful for today?

Date: Week: #

How I spent my life force today.

Affirming the great things in your life.

Ideation and future creation. Write down your inspiring ideas.

"Hope is being able to see that there is light despite all of the darkness."
– Desmond Tutu

How I'm feeling today.

- ☐ Positive
- ☐ Happy
- ☐ Hopeful
- ☐ Grateful
- ☐ Content
- ☐ Alive
- ☐

- ☐ Confident
- ☐ Excited
- ☐ Determined
- ☐ Brave
- ☐ Inspired
- ☐ Proud
- ☐

- ☐ Stressed
- ☐ Frustrated
- ☐ Sad
- ☐ Overwhelmed
- ☐ Angry
- ☐ Nervous
- ☐

- ☐ Restless
- ☐ Trapped
- ☐ Bitter
- ☐ Shocked
- ☐ Guilty
- ☐ Unsure
- ☐

Why I am feeling this way today.

Reflecting on the good. What can you be grateful for today?

Date: Week: #

How I spent my life force today.

Affirming the great things in your life.

Ideation and future creation. Write down your inspiring ideas.

"It is health that is real wealth and not pieces of gold and silver."
– Mahatma Gandhi

FILL YOUR BUCKET LIST

WEEK # _ _ _ _

Your journal is one of the best places to make an actual bucket list.

If you've ever done any goal setting, you know the first step to achieving your goal is to write it down.

Make a list of things you'd like to do, places you'd like to go, or goals you'd like to attain. If you can dream it, you can do it.

Listen to your inner voice! If you're not sure how to begin your list or what to put on it, start by asking yourself a few key questions, such as:

What makes me really happy?
What am I passionate about?

Happy bucket list filling!

Fill your bucket

"Only the weak are cruel. Gentleness can only be expected from the strong."
- Leo Buscaglia

Date: FILL YOUR BUCKET   Week #:

"I can accept failure, everyone fails at something. But I can't accept not trying."
– Michael Jordan

Date: _____   Week: #

How I'm feeling today.

☐ Positive	☐ Confident	☐ Stressed	☐ Restless
☐ Happy	☐ Excited	☐ Frustrated	☐ Trapped
☐ Hopeful	☐ Determined	☐ Sad	☐ Bitter
☐ Grateful	☐ Brave	☐ Overwhelmed	☐ Shocked
☐ Content	☐ Inspired	☐ Angry	☐ Guilty
☐ Alive	☐ Proud	☐ Nervous	☐ Unsure
☐	☐	☐	☐

Why I am feeling this way today.

_____

_____

_____

_____

_____

_____

_____

_____

_____

Reflecting on the good. What can you be grateful for today?

_____

_____

_____

_____

Date: Week: #

How I spent my life force today.

Affirming the great things in your life.

Ideation and future creation. Write down your inspiring ideas.

"Be bold, be brave enough to be your true self."
– Queen Latifah

Date: Week: #

How I'm feeling today.

☐ Positive   ☐ Confident   ☐ Stressed   ☐ Restless
☐ Happy   ☐ Excited   ☐ Frustrated   ☐ Trapped
☐ Hopeful   ☐ Determined   ☐ Sad   ☐ Bitter
☐ Grateful   ☐ Brave   ☐ Overwhelmed   ☐ Shocked
☐ Content   ☐ Inspired   ☐ Angry   ☐ Guilty
☐ Alive   ☐ Proud   ☐ Nervous   ☐ Unsure
☐   ☐   ☐   ☐

Why I am feeling this way today.

_____

_____

_____

_____

_____

_____

_____

_____

_____

Reflecting on the good. What can you be grateful for today?

_____

_____

_____

_____

Date: Week: #

How I spent my life force today.

Affirming the great things in your life.

Ideation and future creation. Write down your inspiring ideas.

"If there is no struggle, there is no progress."
-Frederick Douglass

How I'm feeling today.

- [ ] Positive
- [ ] Happy
- [ ] Hopeful
- [ ] Grateful
- [ ] Content
- [ ] Alive
- [ ]

- [ ] Confident
- [ ] Excited
- [ ] Determined
- [ ] Brave
- [ ] Inspired
- [ ] Proud
- [ ]

- [ ] Stressed
- [ ] Frustrated
- [ ] Sad
- [ ] Overwhelmed
- [ ] Angry
- [ ] Nervous
- [ ]

- [ ] Restless
- [ ] Trapped
- [ ] Bitter
- [ ] Shocked
- [ ] Guilty
- [ ] Unsure
- [ ]

Why I am feeling this way today.

Reflecting on the good. What can you be grateful for today?

Date: Week: #

How I spent my life force today.

Affirming the great things in your life.

Ideation and future creation. Write down your inspiring ideas.

"I have learned over the years that when one's mind is made up, this diminishes fear;
knowing what must be done does away with fear." -Rosa Parks

How I'm feeling today.

☐ Positive ☐ Confident ☐ Stressed ☐ Restless
☐ Happy   ☐ Excited   ☐ Frustrated ☐ Trapped
☐ Hopeful ☐ Determined ☐ Sad   ☐ Bitter
☐ Grateful ☐ Brave   ☐ Overwhelmed ☐ Shocked
☐ Content ☐ Inspired ☐ Angry   ☐ Guilty
☐ Alive   ☐ Proud   ☐ Nervous ☐ Unsure
☐   ☐   ☐

Why I am feeling this way today.

_____

_____

_____

_____

_____

_____

_____

_____

_____

Reflecting on the good. What can you be grateful for today?

_____

_____

_____

_____

Date: Week: #

How I spent my life force today.

Affirming the great things in your life.

Ideation and future creation. Write down your inspiring ideas.

How I'm feeling today.

☐ Positive	☐ Confident	☐ Stressed	☐ Restless
☐ Happy	☐ Excited	☐ Frustrated	☐ Trapped
☐ Hopeful	☐ Determined	☐ Sad	☐ Bitter
☐ Grateful	☐ Brave	☐ Overwhelmed	☐ Shocked
☐ Content	☐ Inspired	☐ Angry	☐ Guilty
☐ Alive	☐ Proud	☐ Nervous	☐ Unsure
☐	☐	☐	☐

Why I am feeling this way today.

Reflecting on the good. What can you be grateful for today?

Date: Week: #

How I spent my life force today.

Affirming the great things in your life.

Ideation and future creation. Write down your inspiring ideas.

"Limits, like fear, is often an illusion."
- Michael Jordan

Date: Week: #

How I'm feeling today.

☐ Positive	☐ Confident	☐ Stressed	☐ Restless
☐ Happy	☐ Excited	☐ Frustrated	☐ Trapped
☐ Hopeful	☐ Determined	☐ Sad	☐ Bitter
☐ Grateful	☐ Brave	☐ Overwhelmed	☐ Shocked
☐ Content	☐ Inspired	☐ Angry	☐ Guilty
☐ Alive	☐ Proud	☐ Nervous	☐ Unsure
☐	☐	☐	☐

Why I am feeling this way today.

Reflecting on the good. What can you be grateful for today?

Date: Week: #

How I spent my life force today.

Affirming the great things in your life.

Ideation and future creation. Write down your inspiring ideas.

"My dear friend, clear your mind of cant."
– Samuel Johnson

Date: _____   Week: #

How I'm feeling today.

- [ ] Positive
- [ ] Happy
- [ ] Hopeful
- [ ] Grateful
- [ ] Content
- [ ] Alive
- [ ]

- [ ] Confident
- [ ] Excited
- [ ] Determined
- [ ] Brave
- [ ] Inspired
- [ ] Proud
- [ ]

- [ ] Stressed
- [ ] Frustrated
- [ ] Sad
- [ ] Overwhelmed
- [ ] Angry
- [ ] Nervous
- [ ]

- [ ] Restless
- [ ] Trapped
- [ ] Bitter
- [ ] Shocked
- [ ] Guilty
- [ ] Unsure
- [ ]

Why I am feeling this way today.

_____

_____

_____

_____

_____

_____

_____

_____

_____

_____

Reflecting on the good. What can you be grateful for today?

_____

_____

_____

_____

Date: Week: #

How I spent my life force today.

_____

_____

_____

_____

_____

_____

_____

_____

_____

Affirming the great things in your life.

_____

_____

_____

_____

Ideation and future creation. Write down your inspiring ideas.

_____

_____

_____

_____

"I never thought a role model should be negative."
– Michael Jordan

YOUR PASSION

WEEK # _ _ _ _

Passion may seem an odd word choice when paired with a career, but rest assured that one of the most important elements of personal happiness is being passionate about your career or your job.

Do not be one of those people who live for the weekends and dread Sunday evenings.

Life is too short to not love the work you do.
Your life is valuable, needed, and worthy of all the wonderful tales you write about in this journal and adventures you have in your life.

This week let's see where your passion, skill, and market needs overlap. This should help with identifying how closely your passion vs. your career aligns.

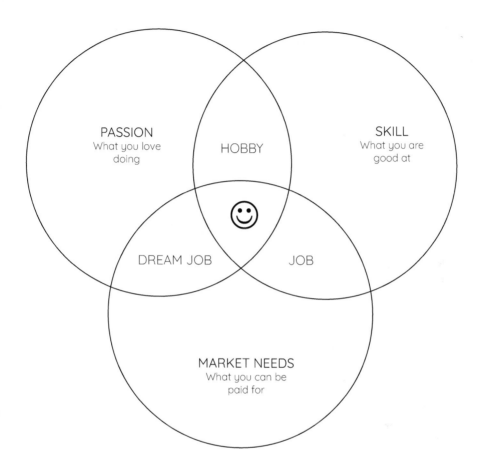

Take a few moments to answer the questions on the next page for some clarity on your passion vs your career,

For each question try to come up with 2-3 answers.
Once you have answered the questions look for themes in your answers.

1. What do you love to do in your free time?

....

....

....

2. What are you a "natural" at?

....

....

....

3. If you could do any job, what would you choose?

....

....

....

4. What types of things energize you?

....

....

....

5. What lifelong interests have you had?

....

....

....

6. Make a list of the values you hold dear?

_____

_____

_____

7. What subject areas do you most enjoy reading about?

_____

_____

_____

8. Your deeply rooted beliefs – your life's calling?

_____

_____

_____

Analyze your responses: What are common themes you
notice? Does anything stand out?

_____

_____

_____

_____

_____

_____

Date: _____   Week: #

How I'm feeling today.

☐ Positive   ☐ Confident   ☐ Stressed   ☐ Restless
☐ Happy   ☐ Excited   ☐ Frustrated   ☐ Trapped
☐ Hopeful   ☐ Determined   ☐ Sad   ☐ Bitter
☐ Grateful   ☐ Brave   ☐ Overwhelmed   ☐ Shocked
☐ Content   ☐ Inspired   ☐ Angry   ☐ Guilty
☐ Alive   ☐ Proud   ☐ Nervous   ☐ Unsure
☐   ☐   ☐   ☐

Why I am feeling this way today.

_____

_____

_____

_____

_____

_____

_____

_____

_____

_____

Reflecting on the good. What can you be grateful for today?

_____

_____

_____

_____

Date: Week: #

How I spent my life force today.

_____

_____

_____

_____

_____

_____

_____

_____

_____

Affirming the great things in your life.

_____

_____

_____

Ideation and future creation. Write down your inspiring ideas.

_____

_____

_____

_____

"Our children may learn about the heroes of the past. Our task is to make ourselves
architects of the future." - Jomo Kenyatta.

Date: _____   Week: #

How I'm feeling today.

☐ Positive	☐ Confident	☐ Stressed	☐ Restless
☐ Happy	☐ Excited	☐ Frustrated	☐ Trapped
☐ Hopeful	☐ Determined	☐ Sad	☐ Bitter
☐ Grateful	☐ Brave	☐ Overwhelmed	☐ Shocked
☐ Content	☐ Inspired	☐ Angry	☐ Guilty
☐ Alive	☐ Proud	☐ Nervous	☐ Unsure
☐	☐	☐	☐

Why I am feeling this way today.

_____

_____

_____

_____

_____

_____

_____

_____

_____

_____

Reflecting on the good. What can you be grateful for today?

_____

_____

_____

_____

_____

Date: Week: #

How I spent my life force today.

Affirming the great things in your life.

Ideation and future creation. Write down your inspiring ideas.

"Ambition never comes to an end."
- - Kenneth Kaunda

Date: _____   Week: #

How I'm feeling today.

☐ Positive   ☐ Confident   ☐ Stressed   ☐ Restless
☐ Happy   ☐ Excited   ☐ Frustrated   ☐ Trapped
☐ Hopeful   ☐ Determined   ☐ Sad   ☐ Bitter
☐ Grateful   ☐ Brave   ☐ Overwhelmed   ☐ Shocked
☐ Content   ☐ Inspired   ☐ Angry   ☐ Guilty
☐ Alive   ☐ Proud   ☐ Nervous   ☐ Unsure
☐   ☐   ☐   ☐

Why I am feeling this way today.

_____

_____

_____

_____

_____

_____

_____

_____

_____

Reflecting on the good. What can you be grateful for today?

_____

_____

_____

_____

_____

Date: Week: #

How I spent my life force today.

Affirming the great things in your life.

Ideation and future creation. Write down your inspiring ideas.

"History has shown us that courage can be contagious, and hope can take on a life of its own.
- Michelle Obama

Date: \qquadWeek: #

How I'm feeling today.

- ☐ Positive
- ☐ Happy
- ☐ Hopeful
- ☐ Grateful
- ☐ Content
- ☐ Alive
- ☐

- ☐ Confident
- ☐ Excited
- ☐ Determined
- ☐ Brave
- ☐ Inspired
- ☐ Proud
- ☐

- ☐ Stressed
- ☐ Frustrated
- ☐ Sad
- ☐ Overwhelmed
- ☐ Angry
- ☐ Nervous
- ☐

- ☐ Restless
- ☐ Trapped
- ☐ Bitter
- ☐ Shocked
- ☐ Guilty
- ☐ Unsure
- ☐

Why I am feeling this way today.

_____

_____

_____

_____

_____

_____

_____

_____

_____

Reflecting on the good. What can you be grateful for today?

_____

_____

_____

_____

Date: Week: #

How I spent my life force today.

Affirming the great things in your life.

Ideation and future creation. Write down your inspiring ideas.

☽

"Defining myself, as opposed to being defined by others,
is one of the most difficult challenges I face." -Carol Moseley-Braun

Date: _____   Week: #

How I'm feeling today.

☐ Positive	☐ Confident	☐ Stressed	☐ Restless
☐ Happy	☐ Excited	☐ Frustrated	☐ Trapped
☐ Hopeful	☐ Determined	☐ Sad	☐ Bitter
☐ Grateful	☐ Brave	☐ Overwhelmed	☐ Shocked
☐ Content	☐ Inspired	☐ Angry	☐ Guilty
☐ Alive	☐ Proud	☐ Nervous	☐ Unsure
☐	☐	☐	☐

Why I am feeling this way today.

_____

_____

_____

_____

_____

_____

_____

_____

_____

_____

Reflecting on the good. What can you be grateful for today?

_____

_____

_____

_____

Date: Week: #

How I spent my life force today.

Affirming the great things in your life.

Ideation and future creation. Write down your inspiring ideas.

"It isn't where you come from; it's where you're going that counts."
-Ella Fitzgerald

Date: Week: #

How I'm feeling today.

☐ Positive	☐ Confident	☐ Stressed	☐ Restless
☐ Happy	☐ Excited	☐ Frustrated	☐ Trapped
☐ Hopeful	☐ Determined	☐ Sad	☐ Bitter
☐ Grateful	☐ Brave	☐ Overwhelmed	☐ Shocked
☐ Content	☐ Inspired	☐ Angry	☐ Guilty
☐ Alive	☐ Proud	☐ Nervous	☐ Unsure
☐	☐	☐	☐

Why I am feeling this way today.

Reflecting on the good. What can you be grateful for today?

Date: Week: #

How I spent my life force today.

Affirming the great things in your life.

Ideation and future creation. Write down your inspiring ideas.

☽

"Every time you state what you want or believe, you're the first to hear it. It's a message to both you
and others about what you think is possible. Don't put a ceiling on yourself." – Oprah Winfrey

Date: _____   Week: #

How I'm feeling today.

☐ Positive   ☐ Confident   ☐ Stressed   ☐ Restless
☐ Happy   ☐ Excited   ☐ Frustrated   ☐ Trapped
☐ Hopeful   ☐ Determined   ☐ Sad   ☐ Bitter
☐ Grateful   ☐ Brave   ☐ Overwhelmed   ☐ Shocked
☐ Content   ☐ Inspired   ☐ Angry   ☐ Guilty
☐ Alive   ☐ Proud   ☐ Nervous   ☐ Unsure
☐   ☐   ☐   ☐

Why I am feeling this way today.

_____

_____

_____

_____

_____

_____

_____

_____

_____

_____

Reflecting on the good. What can you be grateful for today?

_____

_____

_____

_____

Date: Week: #

How I spent my life force today.

_____

_____

_____

_____

_____

_____

_____

_____

_____

Affirming the great things in your life.

_____

_____

_____

Ideation and future creation. Write down your inspiring ideas.

_____

_____

_____

_____

"When I dare to be powerful, to use my strength in the service of my vision,
then it becomes less and less important whether I am afraid." – Audre Lorde

LIMITING BELIEFS

WEEK # _ _ _ _

What could limiting beliefs sound like?

- I have to work hard to earn money.
- I'm not smart enough.
- I'm not worthy.
- I'm too old or too young
- I'll never be successful
- I don't have enough experience
- I need lots of money to start a business.
- Girls don't play soccer, or become astronauts.
- Money is the root of all evil.
- Money does not grow on trees - maybe this one is true.

Limiting beliefs are simply assumptions or opinions that we believe. They come from our life experiences or people in our lives. They are NOT REAL but are false assumptions or opinions that can cause negative outcomes to our hopes and dreams.

Let's start the week by eliminating any limiting beliefs you may have that could be holding you back from living your best life and achieving your dreams.

Reprogram your limiting beliefs

The first step to overcoming your limited beliefs is to:

1. Identify what they are.

2. Recognize that it is just a belief.

3. Challenge your own belief.

4. Realize that your limiting beliefs are potentially damaging.

5. Reframe your limiting belief "it's possible" beliefs.

6. Take action on new beliefs.

Example:

1. Limiting belief: Money is the root to all evil.
2. Recognize: Recognize that this belief comes from someone that may have said this to you at some point.
3. Challenge: There are many people with money making the world a better place.
4. Realize: If you believe money is the route to all evil, it may damage your potential to use money as a tool to do good in the world.
5. Reframe: Money is just a tool that you can use to do good and make the world a better place for you and your family.
6. Take action: Revisit your reframed "it's possible" beliefs often, write them down, and use them as affirmations.

Use the next few pages to start identifying
and reframing your limiting beliefs to "it's possible" beliefs

[Limiting belief:]:

[Recognize:]:

[Challenge:]:

[Realize:]:

[Reframe:]:

[Take action:]:

"The soul that is within me no man can degrade."
- Frederick Douglass

Date: _____   Week: #

How I'm feeling today.

☐ Positive	☐ Confident	☐ Stressed	☐ Restless
☐ Happy	☐ Excited	☐ Frustrated	☐ Trapped
☐ Hopeful	☐ Determined	☐ Sad	☐ Bitter
☐ Grateful	☐ Brave	☐ Overwhelmed	☐ Shocked
☐ Content	☐ Inspired	☐ Angry	☐ Guilty
☐ Alive	☐ Proud	☐ Nervous	☐ Unsure
☐	☐	☐	☐

Why I am feeling this way today.

_____

_____

_____

_____

_____

_____

_____

_____

_____

Reflecting on the good. What can you be grateful for today?

_____

_____

_____

_____

Date: Week: #

How I spent my life force today.

Affirming the great things in your life.

Ideation and future creation. Write down your inspiring ideas.

"History has shown us that courage can be contagious, and hope can take on a life of its own."
-Michelle Obama

How I'm feeling today.

☐ Positive	☐ Confident	☐ Stressed	☐ Restless
☐ Happy	☐ Excited	☐ Frustrated	☐ Trapped
☐ Hopeful	☐ Determined	☐ Sad	☐ Bitter
☐ Grateful	☐ Brave	☐ Overwhelmed	☐ Shocked
☐ Content	☐ Inspired	☐ Angry	☐ Guilty
☐ Alive	☐ Proud	☐ Nervous	☐ Unsure
☐	☐	☐	☐

Why I am feeling this way today.

Reflecting on the good. What can you be grateful for today?

Date: Week: #

How I spent my life force today.

_____

_____

_____

_____

_____

_____

_____

_____

Affirming the great things in your life.

_____

_____

_____

_____

Ideation and future creation. Write down your inspiring ideas.

_____

_____

_____

_____

"Change will not come if we wait for some other person or some other time.
We are the ones we've been waiting for. We are the change that we seek." –Barack Obama

How I'm feeling today.

☐ Positive	☐ Confident	☐ Stressed	☐ Restless
☐ Happy	☐ Excited	☐ Frustrated	☐ Trapped
☐ Hopeful	☐ Determined	☐ Sad	☐ Bitter
☐ Grateful	☐ Brave	☐ Overwhelmed	☐ Shocked
☐ Content	☐ Inspired	☐ Angry	☐ Guilty
☐ Alive	☐ Proud	☐ Nervous	☐ Unsure
☐	☐	☐	☐

Why I am feeling this way today.

Reflecting on the good. What can you be grateful for today?

How I spent my life force today.

Affirming the great things in your life.

Ideation and future creation. Write down your inspiring ideas.

"He who is not courageous enough to take risks will accomplish nothing in life."
– Muhammad Ali

Date: Week: #

How I'm feeling today.

☐ Positive ☐ Confident ☐ Stressed ☐ Restless
☐ Happy ☐ Excited ☐ Frustrated ☐ Trapped
☐ Hopeful ☐ Determined ☐ Sad ☐ Bitter
☐ Grateful ☐ Brave ☐ Overwhelmed ☐ Shocked
☐ Content ☐ Inspired ☐ Angry ☐ Guilty
☐ Alive ☐ Proud ☐ Nervous ☐ Unsure
☐ ☐ ☐ ☐

Why I am feeling this way today.

Reflecting on the good. What can you be grateful for today?

Date: Week: #

How I spent my life force today.

_____

_____

_____

_____

_____

_____

_____

_____

_____

Affirming the great things in your life.

_____

_____

_____

Ideation and future creation. Write down your inspiring ideas.

_____

_____

_____

_____

_____

"If you know whence you came, there is really no limit to where you can go."
—James Baldwin

Date: Week: #

How I'm feeling today.

☐ Positive   ☐ Confident   ☐ Stressed   ☐ Restless
☐ Happy   ☐ Excited   ☐ Frustrated   ☐ Trapped
☐ Hopeful   ☐ Determined   ☐ Sad   ☐ Bitter
☐ Grateful   ☐ Brave   ☐ Overwhelmed   ☐ Shocked
☐ Content   ☐ Inspired   ☐ Angry   ☐ Guilty
☐ Alive   ☐ Proud   ☐ Nervous   ☐ Unsure
☐   ☐   ☐   ☐

Why I am feeling this way today.

Reflecting on the good. What can you be grateful for today?

Date: Week: #

How I spent my life force today.

_____

_____

_____

_____

_____

_____

_____

_____

Affirming the great things in your life.

_____

_____

_____

_____

Ideation and future creation. Write down your inspiring ideas.

_____

_____

_____

_____

"I don't have a feeling of inferiority. Never had. I'm as good as anybody, but no better."
-Katherine Johnson

Date: _____   Week: #

How I'm feeling today.

☐ Positive   ☐ Confident   ☐ Stressed   ☐ Restless
☐ Happy   ☐ Excited   ☐ Frustrated   ☐ Trapped
☐ Hopeful   ☐ Determined   ☐ Sad   ☐ Bitter
☐ Grateful   ☐ Brave   ☐ Overwhelmed   ☐ Shocked
☐ Content   ☐ Inspired   ☐ Angry   ☐ Guilty
☐ Alive   ☐ Proud   ☐ Nervous   ☐ Unsure
☐   ☐   ☐   ☐

Why I am feeling this way today.

_____

_____

_____

_____

_____

_____

_____

_____

_____

_____

Reflecting on the good. What can you be grateful for today?

_____

_____

_____

_____

Date: Week: #

How I spent my life force today.

_____

_____

_____

_____

_____

_____

_____

_____

_____

Affirming the great things in your life.

_____

_____

_____

Ideation and future creation. Write down your inspiring ideas.

_____

_____

_____

_____

"Every great dream begins with a dreamer. Always remember, you have within you the strength, the patience, and the passion to reach for the stars to change the world." – Harriet Tubman

How I'm feeling today.

☐ Positive	☐ Confident	☐ Stressed	☐ Restless
☐ Happy	☐ Excited	☐ Frustrated	☐ Trapped
☐ Hopeful	☐ Determined	☐ Sad	☐ Bitter
☐ Grateful	☐ Brave	☐ Overwhelmed	☐ Shocked
☐ Content	☐ Inspired	☐ Angry	☐ Guilty
☐ Alive	☐ Proud	☐ Nervous	☐ Unsure
☐	☐	☐	☐

Why I am feeling this way today.

Reflecting on the good. What can you be grateful for today?

Date: Week: #

How I spent my life force today.

Affirming the great things in your life.

Ideation and future creation. Write down your inspiring ideas.

"After climbing a great hill, one only finds that there are many more hills to climb."
– Nelson Mandela

BEGIN WITH THE END IN MIND

WEEK # _ _ _ _

In this section, we discover the power of imagination —the ability to envision in your mind what you cannot, at present, see with your eyes.

You always create your dream in your mind first and then in reality.

Make sure that you always keep your bigger dream, purpose, goal, or mission in mind first before you engage in the "how." Never start with "how."

Always start with the dream; the "how" will follow.

The "how" are the stepping stones to your dream.

Take some time this week to define your end goals, your dreams, or mission.

Begin with the end in mind

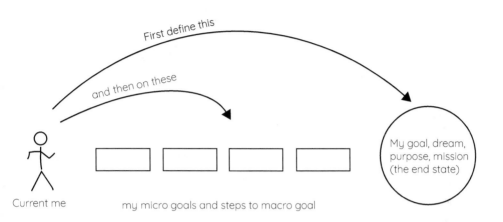

One:
Begin with defining your end goal
(who you want to be or what you want to achieve)

Two:
Clarify your principles, values, and why you want the goal, you defined. This will create and reinforce the motive needed to achieve your goal.

Three:
And finally, plan smaller stepping stones and micro goals and jump into action.

Take some time to define or reflect on each step above, especially beginning with the end in mind.

"The best way to predict the future is to create it."
– Abraham Lincoln

"Hold fast to dreams, for if dreams die, life is a broken-winged bird that cannot fly."
-Langston Hughes

Date: Week: #

How I'm feeling today.

☐ Positive	☐ Confident	☐ Stressed	☐ Restless
☐ Happy	☐ Excited	☐ Frustrated	☐ Trapped
☐ Hopeful	☐ Determined	☐ Sad	☐ Bitter
☐ Grateful	☐ Brave	☐ Overwhelmed	☐ Shocked
☐ Content	☐ Inspired	☐ Angry	☐ Guilty
☐ Alive	☐ Proud	☐ Nervous	☐ Unsure
☐	☐	☐	☐

Why I am feeling this way today.

Reflecting on the good. What can you be grateful for today?

Date: Week: #

How I spent my life force today.

_____

_____

_____

_____

_____

_____

_____

_____

Affirming the great things in your life.

_____

_____

_____

Ideation and future creation. Write down your inspiring ideas.

_____

_____

_____

_____

"Where there is no vision, there is no hope."
- George Washington Carver

How I'm feeling today.

☐ Positive   ☐ Confident   ☐ Stressed   ☐ Restless
☐ Happy   ☐ Excited   ☐ Frustrated   ☐ Trapped
☐ Hopeful   ☐ Determined   ☐ Sad   ☐ Bitter
☐ Grateful   ☐ Brave   ☐ Overwhelmed   ☐ Shocked
☐ Content   ☐ Inspired   ☐ Angry   ☐ Guilty
☐ Alive   ☐ Proud   ☐ Nervous   ☐ Unsure
☐   ☐   ☐   ☐

Why I am feeling this way today.

Reflecting on the good. What can you be grateful for today?

Date: Week: #

How I spent my life force today.

_____

Affirming the great things in your life.

_____

Ideation and future creation. Write down your inspiring ideas.

_____

"I am no longer accepting the things I cannot change. I am changing the things I cannot accept."
– Angela Y. Davis

Date: Week: #

How I'm feeling today.

- [ ] Positive
- [ ] Happy
- [ ] Hopeful
- [ ] Grateful
- [ ] Content
- [ ] Alive
- [ ]

- [ ] Confident
- [ ] Excited
- [ ] Determined
- [ ] Brave
- [ ] Inspired
- [ ] Proud
- [ ]

- [ ] Stressed
- [ ] Frustrated
- [ ] Sad
- [ ] Overwhelmed
- [ ] Angry
- [ ] Nervous
- [ ]

- [ ] Restless
- [ ] Trapped
- [ ] Bitter
- [ ] Shocked
- [ ] Guilty
- [ ] Unsure
- [ ]

Why I am feeling this way today.

Reflecting on the good. What can you be grateful for today?

Date: Week: #

How I spent my life force today.

_____

_____

_____

_____

_____

_____

_____

_____

_____

_____

Affirming the great things in your life.

_____

_____

_____

_____

Ideation and future creation. Write down your inspiring ideas.

_____

_____

_____

_____

"When I look at the future, it's so bright it burns my eyes."
—Oprah Winfrey

How I'm feeling today.

☐ Positive   ☐ Confident   ☐ Stressed   ☐ Restless
☐ Happy   ☐ Excited   ☐ Frustrated   ☐ Trapped
☐ Hopeful   ☐ Determined   ☐ Sad   ☐ Bitter
☐ Grateful   ☐ Brave   ☐ Overwhelmed   ☐ Shocked
☐ Content   ☐ Inspired   ☐ Angry   ☐ Guilty
☐ Alive   ☐ Proud   ☐ Nervous   ☐ Unsure
☐   ☐   ☐   ☐

Why I am feeling this way today.

Reflecting on the good. What can you be grateful for today?

Date: Week: #

How I spent my life force today.

_____

_____

_____

_____

_____

_____

_____

Affirming the great things in your life.

_____

_____

_____

Ideation and future creation. Write down your inspiring ideas.

_____

_____

_____

_____

"You are never too old to set another goal or to dream a new dream."
- Les Brown

Date: _____   Week: #

How I'm feeling today.

☐ Positive	☐ Confident	☐ Stressed	☐ Restless
☐ Happy	☐ Excited	☐ Frustrated	☐ Trapped
☐ Hopeful	☐ Determined	☐ Sad	☐ Bitter
☐ Grateful	☐ Brave	☐ Overwhelmed	☐ Shocked
☐ Content	☐ Inspired	☐ Angry	☐ Guilty
☐ Alive	☐ Proud	☐ Nervous	☐ Unsure
☐	☐	☐	☐

Why I am feeling this way today.

_____

_____

_____

_____

_____

_____

_____

_____

_____

_____

Reflecting on the good. What can you be grateful for today?

_____

_____

_____

_____

_____

Date: Week: #

How I spent my life force today.

Affirming the great things in your life.

Ideation and future creation. Write down your inspiring ideas.

"Open your eyes, look within. Are you satisfied with the life you're living?"
– Bob Marley

Date: \underline{}

\underline{}   Week: #

How I'm feeling today.

☐ Positive	☐ Confident	☐ Stressed	☐ Restless
☐ Happy	☐ Excited	☐ Frustrated	☐ Trapped
☐ Hopeful	☐ Determined	☐ Sad	☐ Bitter
☐ Grateful	☐ Brave	☐ Overwhelmed	☐ Shocked
☐ Content	☐ Inspired	☐ Angry	☐ Guilty
☐ Alive	☐ Proud	☐ Nervous	☐ Unsure
☐	☐	☐	☐

Why I am feeling this way today.

Reflecting on the good. What can you be grateful for today?

Date: Week: #

How I spent my life force today.

Affirming the great things in your life.

Ideation and future creation. Write down your inspiring ideas.

"We can't plan life. All we can do is be available for it."
– Lauryn Hill

Date: Week: #

How I'm feeling today.

☐ Positive	☐ Confident	☐ Stressed	☐ Restless
☐ Happy	☐ Excited	☐ Frustrated	☐ Trapped
☐ Hopeful	☐ Determined	☐ Sad	☐ Bitter
☐ Grateful	☐ Brave	☐ Overwhelmed	☐ Shocked
☐ Content	☐ Inspired	☐ Angry	☐ Guilty
☐ Alive	☐ Proud	☐ Nervous	☐ Unsure
☐	☐	☐	☐

Why I am feeling this way today.

_____

_____

_____

_____

_____

_____

_____

_____

_____

Reflecting on the good. What can you be grateful for today?

_____

_____

_____

_____

Date: Week: #

How I spent my life force today.

Affirming the great things in your life.

Ideation and future creation. Write down your inspiring ideas.

"The time is always right to do what is right."
-Martin Luther King, Jr.

CHOICE, CHANCE, CHANGE

WEEK # _ _ _ _

Choices:
Every day we are faced with decisions – some large, some small. Life can be hard; the path is not always clear.

Chances:
The greatest risk you should avoid at all costs is the risk of doing nothing. Making a choice requires taking a chance. The only regret we usually have is the chances we didn't take.

Changes:
Change is the only constant in life. Yet we fight change. When we embrace change, we open the door to opportunity.

This week, reflect on the choices you may need to make. The chances you'll have taken to move forward towards your goals and the changes you need to make to get you closer to your dream.

Use the additional pages for further reflection.
Don't forget to come back to these sections to see how you have progressed.

Define Dream first

Goals / Dreams

CHANGE

CHANCE

CHOICES

Hard

Choices

_____

_____

_____

Chances

_____

_____

_____

Changes

_____

_____

_____

"I have learned over the years that when one's mind is made up, this diminishes fear; knowing what must be done does away with fear." –Rosa Parks

"Freedom is never given; it is won."
– A. Philip Randolph

How I'm feeling today.

☐ Positive	☐ Confident	☐ Stressed	☐ Restless
☐ Happy	☐ Excited	☐ Frustrated	☐ Trapped
☐ Hopeful	☐ Determined	☐ Sad	☐ Bitter
☐ Grateful	☐ Brave	☐ Overwhelmed	☐ Shocked
☐ Content	☐ Inspired	☐ Angry	☐ Guilty
☐ Alive	☐ Proud	☐ Nervous	☐ Unsure
☐	☐	☐	☐

Why I am feeling this way today.

Reflecting on the good. What can you be grateful for today?

Date: Week: #

How I spent my life force today.

Affirming the great things in your life.

Ideation and future creation. Write down your inspiring ideas.

"The chains of habit are too weak to be felt until they are too strong to be broken."
- Samuel Johnson

How I'm feeling today.

- ☐ Positive
- ☐ Happy
- ☐ Hopeful
- ☐ Grateful
- ☐ Content
- ☐ Alive
- ☐

- ☐ Confident
- ☐ Excited
- ☐ Determined
- ☐ Brave
- ☐ Inspired
- ☐ Proud
- ☐

- ☐ Stressed
- ☐ Frustrated
- ☐ Sad
- ☐ Overwhelmed
- ☐ Angry
- ☐ Nervous
- ☐

- ☐ Restless
- ☐ Trapped
- ☐ Bitter
- ☐ Shocked
- ☐ Guilty
- ☐ Unsure
- ☐

Why I am feeling this way today.

Reflecting on the good. What can you be grateful for today?

Date: Week: #

How I spent my life force today.

_____

_____

_____

_____

_____

_____

_____

_____

Affirming the great things in your life.

_____

_____

_____

_____

Ideation and future creation. Write down your inspiring ideas.

_____

_____

_____

_____

_____

"We will not march back to what was. We move to what shall be, a country that is bruised,
but whole. Benevolent, but bold. Fierce and free." –Amanda Gorman

How I'm feeling today.

☐ Positive	☐ Confident	☐ Stressed	☐ Restless
☐ Happy	☐ Excited	☐ Frustrated	☐ Trapped
☐ Hopeful	☐ Determined	☐ Sad	☐ Bitter
☐ Grateful	☐ Brave	☐ Overwhelmed	☐ Shocked
☐ Content	☐ Inspired	☐ Angry	☐ Guilty
☐ Alive	☐ Proud	☐ Nervous	☐ Unsure
☐	☐	☐	☐

Why I am feeling this way today.

Reflecting on the good. What can you be grateful for today?

Date: Week: #

How I spent my life force today.

_____

_____

_____

_____

_____

_____

_____

_____

Affirming the great things in your life.

_____

_____

_____

_____

Ideation and future creation. Write down your inspiring ideas.

_____

_____

_____

_____

_____

"Even in dark times, we not only dream, we do. We not only see what has been, we see what can be. We shoot for the moon, and then we plant our flag on it." –Kamala Harris

Date: Week: #

How I'm feeling today.

- ☐ Positive
- ☐ Happy
- ☐ Hopeful
- ☐ Grateful
- ☐ Content
- ☐ Alive
- ☐

- ☐ Confident
- ☐ Excited
- ☐ Determined
- ☐ Brave
- ☐ Inspired
- ☐ Proud
- ☐

- ☐ Stressed
- ☐ Frustrated
- ☐ Sad
- ☐ Overwhelmed
- ☐ Angry
- ☐ Nervous
- ☐

- ☐ Restless
- ☐ Trapped
- ☐ Bitter
- ☐ Shocked
- ☐ Guilty
- ☐ Unsure
- ☐

Why I am feeling this way today.

Reflecting on the good. What can you be grateful for today?

Date: Week: #

How I spent my life force today.

Affirming the great things in your life.

Ideation and future creation. Write down your inspiring ideas.

"There are still many causes worth sacrificing for, so much history yet to be made."
—Michelle Obama

How I'm feeling today.

☐ Positive	☐ Confident	☐ Stressed	☐ Restless
☐ Happy	☐ Excited	☐ Frustrated	☐ Trapped
☐ Hopeful	☐ Determined	☐ Sad	☐ Bitter
☐ Grateful	☐ Brave	☐ Overwhelmed	☐ Shocked
☐ Content	☐ Inspired	☐ Angry	☐ Guilty
☐ Alive	☐ Proud	☐ Nervous	☐ Unsure
☐	☐	☐	☐

Why I am feeling this way today.

Reflecting on the good. What can you be grateful for today?

Date: Week: #

How I spent my life force today.

_____

_____

_____

_____

_____

_____

_____

_____

_____

Affirming the great things in your life.

_____

_____

_____

_____

Ideation and future creation. Write down your inspiring ideas.

_____

_____

_____

_____

_____

"I had to make my own living and my own opportunity. But I made it! Don't sit down and wait for the opportunities to come. Get up and make them." —Madam C.J. Walker

How I'm feeling today.

- ☐ Positive
- ☐ Happy
- ☐ Hopeful
- ☐ Grateful
- ☐ Content
- ☐ Alive
- ☐

- ☐ Confident
- ☐ Excited
- ☐ Determined
- ☐ Brave
- ☐ Inspired
- ☐ Proud
- ☐

- ☐ Stressed
- ☐ Frustrated
- ☐ Sad
- ☐ Overwhelmed
- ☐ Angry
- ☐ Nervous
- ☐

- ☐ Restless
- ☐ Trapped
- ☐ Bitter
- ☐ Shocked
- ☐ Guilty
- ☐ Unsure
- ☐

Why I am feeling this way today.

Reflecting on the good. What can you be grateful for today?

Date: Week: #

How I spent my life force today.

Affirming the great things in your life.

Ideation and future creation. Write down your inspiring ideas.

"I had no idea that history was being made. I was just tired of giving up."
– Rosa Parks

Date: _____   Week: #

How I'm feeling today.

☐ Positive   ☐ Confident   ☐ Stressed   ☐ Restless
☐ Happy   ☐ Excited   ☐ Frustrated   ☐ Trapped
☐ Hopeful   ☐ Determined   ☐ Sad   ☐ Bitter
☐ Grateful   ☐ Brave   ☐ Overwhelmed   ☐ Shocked
☐ Content   ☐ Inspired   ☐ Angry   ☐ Guilty
☐ Alive   ☐ Proud   ☐ Nervous   ☐ Unsure
☐   ☐   ☐   ☐

Why I am feeling this way today.

_____

_____

_____

_____

_____

_____

_____

_____

_____

_____

Reflecting on the good. What can you be grateful for today?

_____

_____

_____

_____

_____

Date: Week: #

How I spent my life force today.

Affirming the great things in your life.

Ideation and future creation. Write down your inspiring ideas.

☽

"Diversity is not about how we differ. Diversity is about embracing one another's uniqueness."
- Ola Joseph

THINKING OUTSIDE THE BOX

WEEK # _ _ _ _

Outside the box, thinking is the ability to see many possible answers to a question—it's a fundamental attribute of creativity.

Too often, we are constrained by the reality we perceive; we live in a world of painted boxes that prevent us from divergent thinking and thinking in the realm of possibility.

This is where new ideas are born and new realities created.

Use this week to think outside of the box for just one of the problems or limitations you are facing.

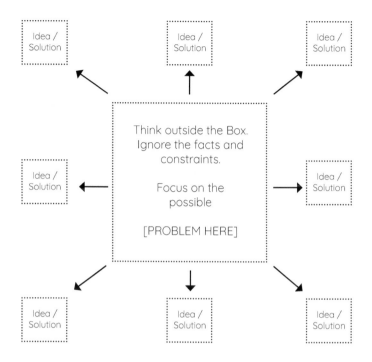

One:
Challenge pre-existing beliefs and recognize that boundary conditions are a choice.

Two:
Challenge assumptions about any aspect of the problem or users.

Three:
Seek alternatives not just alternative potential solutions, but alternative ways of thinking about problems.

"I don't focus on what I'm up against. I focus on my goals and I try to ignore the rest."
– Venus Williams

"The man who has no imagination has no wings."
– Muhammad Ali

How I'm feeling today.

☐ Positive   ☐ Confident   ☐ Stressed   ☐ Restless
☐ Happy   ☐ Excited   ☐ Frustrated   ☐ Trapped
☐ Hopeful   ☐ Determined   ☐ Sad   ☐ Bitter
☐ Grateful   ☐ Brave   ☐ Overwhelmed   ☐ Shocked
☐ Content   ☐ Inspired   ☐ Angry   ☐ Guilty
☐ Alive   ☐ Proud   ☐ Nervous   ☐ Unsure
☐   ☐   ☐   ☐

Why I am feeling this way today.

Reflecting on the good. What can you be grateful for today?

Date: Week: #

How I spent my life force today.

_____

_____

_____

_____

_____

_____

_____

_____

Affirming the great things in your life.

_____

_____

_____

Ideation and future creation. Write down your inspiring ideas.

_____

_____

_____

_____

"Imagine what a harmonious world it could be if every single person,
both young and old shared a little of what he is good at doing." – Quincy Jones

How I'm feeling today.

☐ Positive	☐ Confident	☐ Stressed	☐ Restless
☐ Happy	☐ Excited	☐ Frustrated	☐ Trapped
☐ Hopeful	☐ Determined	☐ Sad	☐ Bitter
☐ Grateful	☐ Brave	☐ Overwhelmed	☐ Shocked
☐ Content	☐ Inspired	☐ Angry	☐ Guilty
☐ Alive	☐ Proud	☐ Nervous	☐ Unsure
☐	☐	☐	☐

Why I am feeling this way today.

Reflecting on the good. What can you be grateful for today?

Date: Week: #

How I spent my life force today.

_____

_____

_____

_____

_____

_____

Affirming the great things in your life.

_____

_____

_____

Ideation and future creation. Write down your inspiring ideas.

_____

_____

_____

_____

"You need imagination in order to imagine a future that doesn't exist."
- Azar Nafisi

How I'm feeling today.

☐ Positive	☐ Confident	☐ Stressed	☐ Restless
☐ Happy	☐ Excited	☐ Frustrated	☐ Trapped
☐ Hopeful	☐ Determined	☐ Sad	☐ Bitter
☐ Grateful	☐ Brave	☐ Overwhelmed	☐ Shocked
☐ Content	☐ Inspired	☐ Angry	☐ Guilty
☐ Alive	☐ Proud	☐ Nervous	☐ Unsure
☐	☐	☐	☐

Why I am feeling this way today.

Reflecting on the good. What can you be grateful for today?

Date: Week: #

How I spent my life force today.

_____

_____

_____

_____

_____

_____

_____

_____

Affirming the great things in your life.

_____

_____

_____

Ideation and future creation. Write down your inspiring ideas.

_____

_____

_____

_____

Date: _____   '   Week: #

How I'm feeling today.

☐ Positive   ☐ Confident   ☐ Stressed   ☐ Restless
☐ Happy   ☐ Excited   ☐ Frustrated   ☐ Trapped
☐ Hopeful   ☐ Determined   ☐ Sad   ☐ Bitter
☐ Grateful   ☐ Brave   ☐ Overwhelmed   ☐ Shocked
☐ Content   ☐ Inspired   ☐ Angry   ☐ Guilty
☐ Alive   ☐ Proud   ☐ Nervous   ☐ Unsure
☐   ☐   ☐   ☐

Why I am feeling this way today.

_____

_____

_____

_____

_____

_____

_____

_____

_____

Reflecting on the good. What can you be grateful for today?

_____

_____

_____

_____

Date: Week: #

How I spent my life force today.

Affirming the great things in your life.

Ideation and future creation. Write down your inspiring ideas.

"Imagination and fiction make up more than three quarters of our real life."
— Simone Weil

How I'm feeling today.

☐ Positive	☐ Confident	☐ Stressed	☐ Restless
☐ Happy	☐ Excited	☐ Frustrated	☐ Trapped
☐ Hopeful	☐ Determined	☐ Sad	☐ Bitter
☐ Grateful	☐ Brave	☐ Overwhelmed	☐ Shocked
☐ Content	☐ Inspired	☐ Angry	☐ Guilty
☐ Alive	☐ Proud	☐ Nervous	☐ Unsure
☐	☐	☐	☐

Why I am feeling this way today.

_____

_____

_____

_____

_____

_____

_____

_____

_____

Reflecting on the good. What can you be grateful for today?

_____

_____

_____

_____

_____

Date: Week: #

How I spent my life force today.

_____

_____

_____

_____

_____

_____

_____

_____

Affirming the great things in your life.

_____

_____

_____

Ideation and future creation. Write down your inspiring ideas.

_____

_____

_____

_____

"I have fallen in love with the imagination. And if you fall in love with the imagination,
you understand that it is a free spirit. It will go anywhere, and it can do anything." – Alice Walker

Date: _____   Week: #

How I'm feeling today.

☐ Positive   ☐ Confident   ☐ Stressed   ☐ Restless
☐ Happy   ☐ Excited   ☐ Frustrated   ☐ Trapped
☐ Hopeful   ☐ Determined   ☐ Sad   ☐ Bitter
☐ Grateful   ☐ Brave   ☐ Overwhelmed   ☐ Shocked
☐ Content   ☐ Inspired   ☐ Angry   ☐ Guilty
☐ Alive   ☐ Proud   ☐ Nervous   ☐ Unsure
☐   ☐   ☐   ☐

Why I am feeling this way today.

_____

_____

_____

_____

_____

_____

_____

_____

_____

Reflecting on the good. What can you be grateful for today?

_____

_____

_____

_____

_____

Date: Week: #

How I spent my life force today.

_____

_____

_____

_____

_____

_____

_____

_____

_____

Affirming the great things in your life.

_____

_____

_____

Ideation and future creation. Write down your inspiring ideas.

_____

_____

_____

_____

"Help others achieve their dreams and you will achieve yours."
- Les Brown

Date: _____   Week: #

How I'm feeling today.

☐ Positive   ☐ Confident   ☐ Stressed   ☐ Restless
☐ Happy   ☐ Excited   ☐ Frustrated   ☐ Trapped
☐ Hopeful   ☐ Determined   ☐ Sad   ☐ Bitter
☐ Grateful   ☐ Brave   ☐ Overwhelmed   ☐ Shocked
☐ Content   ☐ Inspired   ☐ Angry   ☐ Guilty
☐ Alive   ☐ Proud   ☐ Nervous   ☐ Unsure
☐   ☐   ☐   ☐

Why I am feeling this way today.

_____
_____
_____
_____
_____
_____
_____
_____
_____
_____

Reflecting on the good. What can you be grateful for today?

_____
_____
_____
_____

Date:

How I spent my life force today.

Affirming the great things in your life.

Ideation and future creation. Write down your inspiring ideas.

"If there is a book that you want to read, but it hasn't been written yet,
you must be the one to write it." —Toni Morrison

DREAM CASTING

WEEK # _ _ _ _

Everything you see and touch around you comes from someone's imagination. They were Dream Casting the future into reality. This is what Dream Casting is, creating the future with your dreams.

It's this wonderful truth that allows your dreams to became a possibility - a real-world reality.

So don't settle for being a non-player character, be the conjurer, a dream caster of your own world.

Perfect Me: Dream Cast how you want to see yourself starting today?. Remeber you are alredy perfectly imperfect!

_____

_____

My Family/Friends: Dream Cast how your family/friend relationships look like in your perfect world?

_____

_____

My Career: Dream Cast what your ideal job looks like? Describe it here.

_____

_____

The Impossible: Dream Cast the things you want to achieve but seem impossible? Write down your ideas.

_____

_____

Travel: list Dream Cast your travel list ond where you want to go? Write down your dream destinations.

_____

_____

_____

Finances: Dream Cast your financial situation in a perfect world?
e.g. debt free, comfortable, etc..

- -

- -

- -

Health/Fitness: Dream Cast what you would change about your
health and fitness.

- -

- -

- -

Adventures: Dream Cast all the the adventures you would like to
complete.

- -

- -

- -

Paying it forward: You have been given so much in terms of talent
and knowledge. Dream Cast how you could pay it forward.

- -

- -

- -

☐

- -

- -

- -

"A man's worth is no greater than his ambitions."
- Marcus Aurelius

Date: DREAM CASTING Week #:

"The future rewards those who press on. I don't have time to feel sorry for myself.
I don't have time to complain. I'm going to press on." – Barack Obama

Date: _____   Week: #

How I'm feeling today.

☐ Positive	☐ Confident	☐ Stressed	☐ Restless
☐ Happy	☐ Excited	☐ Frustrated	☐ Trapped
☐ Hopeful	☐ Determined	☐ Sad	☐ Bitter
☐ Grateful	☐ Brave	☐ Overwhelmed	☐ Shocked
☐ Content	☐ Inspired	☐ Angry	☐ Guilty
☐ Alive	☐ Proud	☐ Nervous	☐ Unsure
☐	☐	☐	☐

Why I am feeling this way today.

_____

_____

_____

_____

_____

_____

_____

_____

_____

_____

Reflecting on the good. What can you be grateful for today?

_____

_____

_____

_____

Date: Week: #

How I spent my life force today.

Affirming the great things in your life.

Ideation and future creation. Write down your inspiring ideas.

☽

"Every great dream begins with a dreamer. Always remember, you have within you the strength, the patience, and the passion to reach for the stars to change the world." –Harriet Tubman

How I'm feeling today.

☐ Positive	☐ Confident	☐ Stressed	☐ Restless
☐ Happy	☐ Excited	☐ Frustrated	☐ Trapped
☐ Hopeful	☐ Determined	☐ Sad	☐ Bitter
☐ Grateful	☐ Brave	☐ Overwhelmed	☐ Shocked
☐ Content	☐ Inspired	☐ Angry	☐ Guilty
☐ Alive	☐ Proud	☐ Nervous	☐ Unsure
☐	☐	☐	☐

Why I am feeling this way today.

Reflecting on the good. What can you be grateful for today?

Date: Week: #

How I spent my life force today.

_____

_____

_____

_____

_____

_____

_____

_____

_____

Affirming the great things in your life.

_____

_____

_____

Ideation and future creation. Write down your inspiring ideas.

_____

_____

_____

_____

☽

"What's the world for if you can't make it up the way you want it?"
-Toni Morrison

How I'm feeling today.

☐ Positive   ☐ Confident   ☐ Stressed   ☐ Restless
☐ Happy   ☐ Excited   ☐ Frustrated   ☐ Trapped
☐ Hopeful   ☐ Determined   ☐ Sad   ☐ Bitter
☐ Grateful   ☐ Brave   ☐ Overwhelmed   ☐ Shocked
☐ Content   ☐ Inspired   ☐ Angry   ☐ Guilty
☐ Alive   ☐ Proud   ☐ Nervous   ☐ Unsure
☐   ☐   ☐   ☐

Why I am feeling this way today.

Reflecting on the good. What can you be grateful for today?

Date: Week: #

How I spent my life force today.

_____

_____

_____

_____

_____

_____

_____

_____

Affirming the great things in your life.

_____

_____

_____

_____

Ideation and future creation. Write down your inspiring ideas.

_____

_____

_____

_____

"Whatever we believe about ourselves and our ability comes true for us."
-Susan L. Taylor

How I'm feeling today.

- ☐ Positive
- ☐ Happy
- ☐ Hopeful
- ☐ Grateful
- ☐ Content
- ☐ Alive
- ☐

- ☐ Confident
- ☐ Excited
- ☐ Determined
- ☐ Brave
- ☐ Inspired
- ☐ Proud
- ☐

- ☐ Stressed
- ☐ Frustrated
- ☐ Sad
- ☐ Overwhelmed
- ☐ Angry
- ☐ Nervous
- ☐

- ☐ Restless
- ☐ Trapped
- ☐ Bitter
- ☐ Shocked
- ☐ Guilty
- ☐ Unsure
- ☐

Why I am feeling this way today.

Reflecting on the good. What can you be grateful for today?

Date:

How I spent my life force today.

Affirming the great things in your life.

Ideation and future creation. Write down your inspiring ideas.

🌙

"I was walking through Harvard in the evening, and a Black woman I did not know was passing me on the sidewalk ... She leaned over as we crossed and said, 'Persevere.'" –Ketanji Brown Jackson

Date: _____   Week: #

How I'm feeling today.

☐ Positive	☐ Confident	☐ Stressed	☐ Restless
☐ Happy	☐ Excited	☐ Frustrated	☐ Trapped
☐ Hopeful	☐ Determined	☐ Sad	☐ Bitter
☐ Grateful	☐ Brave	☐ Overwhelmed	☐ Shocked
☐ Content	☐ Inspired	☐ Angry	☐ Guilty
☐ Alive	☐ Proud	☐ Nervous	☐ Unsure
☐	☐	☐	☐

Why I am feeling this way today.

_____

_____

_____

_____

_____

_____

_____

_____

_____

_____

Reflecting on the good. What can you be grateful for today?

_____

_____

_____

_____

_____

Date: Week: #

How I spent my life force today.

Affirming the great things in your life.

Ideation and future creation. Write down your inspiring ideas.

"Education is transformational. It changes lives. Its the force that erases arbitrary divisions of race and class and culture and unlocks every person's God-given potential." –Condoleezza Rice

Date: _____   Week: #

How I'm feeling today.

☐ Positive   ☐ Confident   ☐ Stressed   ☐ Restless
☐ Happy   ☐ Excited   ☐ Frustrated   ☐ Trapped
☐ Hopeful   ☐ Determined   ☐ Sad   ☐ Bitter
☐ Grateful   ☐ Brave   ☐ Overwhelmed   ☐ Shocked
☐ Content   ☐ Inspired   ☐ Angry   ☐ Guilty
☐ Alive   ☐ Proud   ☐ Nervous   ☐ Unsure
☐   ☐   ☐   ☐

Why I am feeling this way today.

_____

_____

_____

_____

_____

_____

_____

_____

_____

_____

Reflecting on the good. What can you be grateful for today?

_____

_____

_____

_____

Date: Week: #

How I spent my life force today.

Affirming the great things in your life.

Ideation and future creation. Write down your inspiring ideas.

"The best way to make dreams come true is to wake up."
—Mae C. Jemison

Date: Week: #

How I'm feeling today.

☐ Positive	☐ Confident	☐ Stressed	☐ Restless
☐ Happy	☐ Excited	☐ Frustrated	☐ Trapped
☐ Hopeful	☐ Determined	☐ Sad	☐ Bitter
☐ Grateful	☐ Brave	☐ Overwhelmed	☐ Shocked
☐ Content	☐ Inspired	☐ Angry	☐ Guilty
☐ Alive	☐ Proud	☐ Nervous	☐ Unsure
☐	☐	☐	☐

Why I am feeling this way today.

_____

_____

_____

_____

_____

_____

_____

_____

_____

_____

Reflecting on the good. What can you be grateful for today?

_____

_____

_____

_____

_____

Date: Week: #

How I spent my life force today.

Affirming the great things in your life.

Ideation and future creation. Write down your inspiring ideas.

"You have to dream before your dreams can come true."
— A. P. J. Abdul Kalam

You've used all your paper

Congratulations, you've used up all your paper - this is a milestone and only the beginning of your amazing journey of becoming you and living your best life.

You have achieved something great and should be very proud of yourself.

We hope that your journal will be a reminder of all that you are capable of, of everything that you dreamed of and achieved over the past few months.

Your journey is worth penning; continue your journey towards your best life.

"Journal writing gives
us insights into,
who we are,
who we were,
and
who we can become."

Share:
@dreamcastproject #dreamcastproject

Suport:
hello@dreamcastproject.com

Shop:
www.dreamcastproject.com

Becoming You Journal
Version 2
ISBN: 978-1-7377348-2-6
Published by Parent Diary LLC, The

Need more paper?

We've created the daily "Becoming You" journal pages separately so that you can continue your awesome journey.
They are just the daily pages without the topics.

Each journal has 90 days of pages and is perfect for your daily reflection.

Visit www.dreamcastproject.com

"I will not take 'but' for an answer."
– Langston Hughes

Made in the USA
Columbia, SC
01 November 2023

25341531R00124